Published by Murdoch Carberry
97 Park Winding, Erskine PA8 7AT

Printed by Orr, Pollock & Co. Ltd.
2 Crawfurd Street, Greenock PA15 1LH

Typesetting by Kelvin Technical Publishing Ltd
4 Bowmont Gardens, Glasgow G12 9LR

First Published 1988

ISBN 0 9513574 0 9

For Susan

Front cover: The Cunard liner *Sylvania* is shown, almost ready
                for launching, at John Brown's shipyard in Clyde-
                bank, November 1956.

Back cover: Houseflags illustration by Alan McKay

Working in the Shipyards illustrated by James Smith.

BETTER BY YARDS

Colin M. Castle

In my early days I was afraid to come to John Brown's because the requirements were so high, and I felt as a tradesman that I might not meet up with what they wanted. So that when I did come in here eventually, I felt an immense pride.

Shipyard Worker, 1967

CONTENTS

ACKNOWLEDGEMENTS

I would like to thank the following people for their assistance in obtaining material for this book: Staff at the Glasgow Museum of Transport, staff of the Glasgow Room at the Mitchell Library, Glasgow; Keith Robinson, Director of the Scottish Centre for Social Subjects; Michael Moss, Senior Archivist at Glasgow University; Staff of the National Maritime Museum; Trustees of the Imperial War Museum; Miss Pat Malcolm, Reference Librarian, Clydebank District Library; Ian McCrorie; and John Cumming. Thanks to Jack Mulrine, Frank McElvey, Charles MacPherson and Michael Harrigan for their reminiscences on shipyard life. Finally I would like to express my gratitude to C E Langmuir and all those who read and commented helpfully on the manuscript.

Illustrations

Most of the illustrations in this book come from the author's personal collection. Many are art cards published originally by the shipping companies themselves or were part of the 'Oilette' series of postcards issued by the Raphael Tuck Company. Only the finest marine artists of the day undertook commissions for the various mercantile fleets and today their works are highly prized by collectors. Among the best known artists were Odin Rosenvinge, whose *Aquitania*, *Tuscania* and *Circassia* are represented here, Charles Dixon-the *Ophir*, C E Turner - the *Saxonia*. Other noted artists included Kenneth Shoesmith, Norman Wilkinson, Montague Black and James S Mann. The Raphael Tuck Company employed a battery of artists who contributed outstanding masterpieces to the 'Great Liners' series of which the views of the *Lusitania*, *Virginian*, *Orsova* and *Campania* are worthy examples. Postcard photographic studies account for most of the remaining visuals including the *Duchess of York*, *Empress of Britain*, *Caronia* and the QE2.

SHIPBUILDING ON THE CLYDE

The Clyde Docks

Glasgow merchants owned trading vessels as far back as 1420 but it was not until the 1830's that ships of any appreciable size could sail up the river to the city. Even during the prosperous reign of the Tobacco Lords supplies destined for city warehouses were unloaded at Port Glasgow further down the Firth and transported by cart or pack-horse. Indeed Port Glasgow owes its very existence to the unnavigable nature of the Clyde's upper reaches. Responsibility for maintaining and improving the Clyde lay with the Clyde Navigation Trust, established by Act of Parliament in 1759. Deepening commenced around 1770 and continued for the next hundred years or so. In one fifty year period alone 58 million cubic yards of material was dredged from the river, lowering its bed by between 24 to 29 feet. As a result of such measures Robert Napier of Glasgow was able, in the 1840's, to construct and launch the first Cunarders from his shipyard in Govan.

Princes dock early 1900's

Shipbuilding and shipping advanced side by side. Kingston Dock, Glasgow's first tidal dock with five acres of water space, was opened in 1867 and was a considerable improvement on the older quays. This was followed ten years later by the much larger Queen's Dock, of thirty-four acres, which became closely identified with ships of the Anchor Line whose *Victoria* was the first to use it. By 1858 there was a full size graving-dock at Tod and MacGregor's yard at the mouth of the Kelvin and another larger version was opened opposite the Queen's Dock in 1875. Prince's Dock and Yorkhill Docks, opened 1897 and 1909 respectively, formed the western terminus for city-bound ships. With the opening in July 1931 of the Rothesay Dock at Clydebank and the King George V Dock on the south side of the river, an era of expansion began which was to take the harbour within sight of Port Glasgow once more. Even so the ever expanding number of docks and wharves barely kept pace with the thriving shipping trade and the increasing tonnage of goods being handled by the port. In 1860 this had stood at 1,200,000 tons but by 1900 the figure was six times greater, making Glasgow the third British port after Liverpool and London according to net registry.

Glasgow Shipping Companies

The development and deepening of the Clyde was soon exploited by Glasgow merchants and created a firm foundation upon which several notable city-based firms were built.

George Smith (1803-1876) was a small businessman who was convinced that there was a market for his goods in the Indian sub-continent, part of the world he knew little or nothing about. With a single-mindedness which few of his colleagues could understand he determined to buy a ship and open up a trade with India. Within a few years Smith had a monopoly of the Calcutta and Bombay trade. His success was attributed to an insistence on punctuality of service, reasonable freight rates and an acute business acumen. An avowed supporter of the steamship he purchased several of these in 1869 when the Suez Canal opened, renouncing sail completely. One of his first ships bore the name *City of Glasgow* and subsequently all Smith vessels were named after cities, hence the birth of the City Line.

6

Not everyone in the mercantile trade rejected sail however. In the latter half of the nineteenth century steam power was still a hit-and-miss affair, especially on the long-haul routes to Australia and the Far East. Several Glasgow shipping firms, among them the Loch Line, Shire Line, Bank Line and Port Line, for a time carved a slice of the commercial market by remaining firmly devoted to sail.

The emigrant trade was a profitable one which shipowners were quick to identify. The Clan Line, established in Liverpool in 1878, was one of the first to ferry thousands of Scots, Irish and mid-Europeans to a new life in Canada and rapidly became the largest of all the Glasgow shipping companies. In 1880 the Board of Directors moved their centre of operations to Glasgow and from that time Clan Line vessels became associated with routes to South and East Africa and India. Patrick Henderson, a native of Fife, did much the same thing on the New Zealand route between 1865 and 1882 although the company later became strongly identified with the Burma trade. Finding cargoes for the return journey from New Zealand posed a problem for the firm which led them to divert their ships to Rangoon where cargoes of teak and rice were readily available. In time Henderson would found the Irrawaddy Flotilla Company which boasted one of the largest fleets of river craft in the world, around 650, at the outbreak of World War Two.

EGYPT   HENDERSON LINE   BURMA

The Glen Line was founded by the Gows and the MacGregors, two Scottish families of humble Highland origins. In the mid-1800's they set up several shipbroking and cargo trading businesses and chose Glasgow as the centre of their operations. The families were brought together by a shared interest in shipbuilding and its associated technologies. Jointly they established the London and Glasgow Engineering and Iron Shipbuilding Company Limited which later became the Clydeside yard of Harland and Wolff. James MacGregor was among the first to appreciate the commercial advantages offered by the opening of the Suez Canal and put these to the test in November 1870 when his vessel, the *Glengyle*, made her maiden voyage from London to Madras and Calcutta. She returned in July of the following year having made a gross dividend of 30% on the voyage. In 1874 MacGregor and Gow merged their shipping operations and concentrated on developing the Far East-New York trade and the profitable tea trade with China. The Elder-Dempster Line acquired in 1911 a controlling interest in the company and nine years later merged it with another of their acquisitions, the smaller Shire Line. The Glen Line board were quick to show an interest in diesel-engined ships and ordered the *Glengyle* and the *Glenapp* from Harland and Wolff and Barclay Curle respectively. These were Britain's largest pioneering motor cargo vessels. For much of the 1920's the company continued to play a dominant role in the China trade, concentrating their activities on Shanghai and the North China routes.

In 1862 Donald Currie resigned his position as a senior Cunard official to set up his own business. He initially operated a fleet of sailing ships on the London to India route but branched out into steamship operations at a later date by establishing the Liverpool and Hamburg Line. In 1872, Currie agreed to operate ships on South African routes following an urgent invitation to do so by a group of influential Cape merchants; this group had become alarmed at the complacency of the Union Line which then had a virtual monopoly on Cape trading. So successful was this venture that Currie was offered a half-share in the Royal Mail contract when it came up for renewal in 1876. For the next twenty-four years the Union Line and Currie's Castle Line competed intensively on the South African trade routes. This had the effect of reducing passage times from twenty three days to seventeen, with a corresponding increase in the size of vessels from 2,500 tons to over 12,000 tons. Late in 1899 the Castle Line acquired the assets of its rival and a new company, the renowned Union-Castle Line, was established in March of the following year.

For over a hundred years the Anchor Line's ships played a leading role in linking Scotland with America and India. The company was founded in 1838 by two brothers , Nicol and Robert Handyside, and traded firstly under the name N & R Handyside. They used chartered tonnage, having no vessels of their own, but by 1852 the brothers had a financial stake in two ships and determined to branch out into ship owning. It was at this time that the company came to be known as the Anchor Line but only for advertising purposes. For the next fifteen years trade was mainly confined to the Mediterranean with the company taking the bold step of inaugurating on 30th October 1869, using the vessel *Tyrian*, the first regular steamship service between the Mediterranean and New York. A month later the Anchor Line's *Dido* became the first British vessel to pass through the newly opened Suez Canal and for the company this led to a rapid growth in their India trade. By this time the Anchor Line was under the control of the four Henderson Brothers, Thomas, John, David and William, whose shrewd business sense made them acutely aware of market needs and how to develop them. David and William founded the Finnieston Steamship Works

Company, building engines for hulls, but the firm became known as D & W Henderson when it started shipbuilding at Meadowside in the yard previously ocupied by tod and MacGregor. It was to this company that the Anchor Line went for many of its ships. John and Thomas were principally involved in the running of the line itself. Anchor developed into one of the foremost shipping companies of the day, rivalling both Inman and Cunard on the North Atlantic and offering stiff competition to the numerous lines intent on exploiting trade links with the 'jewel in the crown'. On the important American routes the Anchor Line had established as early as 1865 a regular weekly service which proved to be a lucrative source of income for the firm. This was largely due to the growth of the emigrant trade which declined only around 1914. In the first decade of the twentieth century the company was at the height of its fortunes with a fleet of thirty-two vessels operating on routes to America, Canada, India and the Mediterranean.

Ships of the Donaldson fleet were another familiar sight on the Clyde. The firm was founded in 1855 by William Falconer Donaldson and his brother John and traded under the name of Donaldson Brothers. To begin with they dealt in ship brokerage, chartering and insurance but by the 1860's the company had fleets of ships, most of which were chartered sailing vessels, operating on routes to South America and the Far East. In 1870 the Donaldsons introduced steamships, specially built for the company, on the South American route. The *Astarte* inaugurated the service, but it was her sister *Marina* which had the distinction in 1874 of opening what was to become the Donaldson Line's principal route-the Canada run. Once again the attraction was the emigrant trade whose numbers then showed no sign of abating. By 1900 the company was operating on the following routes: Glasgow to Valparaiso; Glasgow to Montreal in summer, St John, New Brunswick in winter; Glasgow to Baltimore and Bristol to Montreal. The years after the Great War saw the family business at its peak with outright control of three companies-Donaldson Line, Donaldson Atlantic Line and Donaldson South American Line-and a substantial share in the Anchor-Donaldson Line, a partnership formed in 1916.

Pride of place among the Glasgow-based shipping lines must however, be given to the Allan Line. Alexander Allan, a cousin of Robert Burns, was the company's founder. Five of his nine children went on to establish the business formally, calling it the Montreal

Ocean Steamship Company. So successful was the Allan Line on the Canadian route that by the end of the nineteenth century it was carrying one and a half times the capacity of its nearest rivals. In 1891 the company absorbed the smaller State Line, gaining six ships in the process, so that by 1900 its fleet ran to 32 vessels. From 1887 the Allan Line had a strong rival in the Canadian Pacific and in an effort to maintain a lead the company ordered two new turbine ships, the *Victorian* and *Virginian*, to compete against CPR's older triple expansion engined vessels. Passenger accommodation in both was of a high standard forcing CPR to reply with their *Empress of Britain* and *Empress of Ireland*. Sadly the Allan Line's lead was short lived and its assets were sold to CPR in 1909 for $8.5 million. Allan's South American service was hived off to the Donaldson Line in 1913 and the line was wholly absorbed by CPR in 1916 when it was just two years short of its century. It is still regarded by many as the doyen of Glasgow shipping lines.

In some cases major shipping lines, while not necessarily Glasgow-based, owed their existence in part to the efforts of Glasgow traders, engineers, businessmen and shipbuilders. There is no better example of this than the Cunard Line which, in its formative years, had on its board of directors George Burns (of G & J Burns, later Burns and Laird) and Robert Napier. Napier was primarily responsible for building the company's first four trans-Atlantic steamships and his yard would subsequently build several Cunard 'fliers' long after its founder had severed all links with the firm in 1860.

Major Glasgow based shipping lines circa 1900

Operating Steamships		Operating Sailing Ships	
Clan Line	41	Shire Line	27
Anchor Line	32	Loch Line	16
Allan Line	32	Port Line	10
Burrell and Son	27	County Line	9
MacLay and MacIntyre	47		
City Line	21		
Donaldson Line	9		
J & P Hutcheson	11		

Eventually some of the Glasgow based shipping companies would be taken over or merged with their rivals, either from a corporate or operational standpoint, eg. Cunard-Anchor, CPR-Allan and Ellerman-City. The merged companies formed and maintained strong commercial links with the city; thus at the height of the city's trading prosperity her docks had vessels of every major shipping line loading and unloading for as far as the eye could see. Regular visitors to the port, in addition to those mentioned above were: Blue Funnel Ships; Bibby Line Ships; ships of the Orient, P & O, British India and Lamport and Holt Lines. Vessels from Europe, Africa, the West Indies, South America, New Zealand and Australia, the United States and the Far East had Glasgow as their destination at some point in their careers; all of which helped to make her the 'Second City of the Empire'.

The Clyde Shipyards

Growth of Clyde Shipbuilding

Although shipbuilding had existed on the Clyde for many centuries, it did so only in embryonic form until the eighteenth century. The subsequent rise in the fortunes of the tobacco and sugar merchants of Glasgow made the ownership of large fleets a necessity and it was to America, where timber was in plentiful supply, that these entrepreneurs first looked for vessels. The War of Independence (1775-1783) put a stop to such trade, forcing merchants to buy ships from local builders. Some yards, such as Scotts of Greenock, were already well established by this time, but the demands of local and international commerce prompted further development of the industry.

A related factor in the growth of Clyde shipbuilding was the importance of Glasgow and the surrounding area, where factories had started to use steam power, in the textile market . Thanks largely to the work of pioneers like Greenock-born James Watt the many applications of the steam engine soon became apparent. In 1802 William Symington's *Charlotte Dundas* proved herself capable of towing cargoes at a sustained speed on the Forth and Clyde Canal and a decade later Henry Bell's *Comet* was providing the Firth with the world's first regular steamboat service.

During these early years of steamship construction wooden hulls were built by firms on the lower reaches of the river and their engines were fabricated in Glasgow. Unquestionably, the most influential pioneers at this time were the Napier family who om 1836 opened a marine engineering works at Lancefield opposite the mouth of the Kelvin. Robert Napier in particular sought to improve machinery performance and the firm prospered under his guidance. It became the training ground for the next generation of shipbuilders-people like William Denny, James and George Thomson, John Elder and William Pearce all learned their trades there.

The Clyde yards were quick to adopt the techniques of iron shipbuilding and it was the firm of Tod and MacGregor which opened the first iron shipyard in 1834. Robert Napier began a similar enterprise in 1841, selling iron ships mainly to firms where he was employed as an engineer or financial adviser eg. the Isle of Man Steam Packet Company and the British and North American Steam Packet Company. Eventually the success of these vessels convinced both Lloyds of London and the Admiralty of their soundness. Iron ships were more expensive to build but their running costs were 25% less than those of a wooden hulled ship. In the period from 1860 to 1870 the Clyde yards built 800,000 tons of iron ships and larger yards were laid out to meet the ever more ambitious demands of customers. Some yards began to specialise eg. Simons of Renfrew which concentrated on the construction of dredgers while Russell and Company of Port Glasgow saw their future in large sailing ships, which were the cargo carriers of their day. Such was the development of Clyde shipbuilding that in 1870 its output accounted for 70% of national tonnage compared with a mere 5% in 1835.

With the introduction of mild steel, boiler pressures could be increased allowing a corresponding improvement in engine performance. By 1889 97% of all Clyde-built ships were constructed of steel, with production rising to an unprecedented 750,000 tons in 1913. The reasons for such rapid growth were the final demise of sail, a switch by owners to the purchase of tramp steamers and the adoption of the revolutionary steam turbine engine. Clydeside had then established an ascendancy in shipbuilding which ensured that the names of its yards and the skills of its craftsmen would be known throughout the world.

Many shipyards helped to create the Clyde shipbuilding legend, among them Barclay Curle, Charles Connel, Harland and Wolff, William Beardmore, A & J Inglis and the lesser known earlier yards of Cairds, T B Seath, Tod and MacGregor and Randolph, Elder and Co. An extensive listing of the principal Clyde shipbuilders is given in Appendix A, while short accounts of the origins and achievements of seven major yards are presented here.

Scott's Shipbuilding and Engineering Company
The oldest of the Clyde yards, Scott's dates back to 1711 when John Scott began building fishing smacks at Greenock. Successive generations took the firm to greater heights so that by the end of the eighteenth century ocean-going vessels were being constructed. Scott's was a progressive yard which for a time led the way in matters of design and construction technique. They opened the first graving dock in 1767 and produced two paddle steamers, *Active* and *Despatch*, in 1815. A long history of marine engineering began with the purchase of an iron and brass foundry, which traded under the name of Scott, Sinclair and Company and later the Greenock Foundry before being absorbed into the parent company in 1904.

14

The Greenock yard also had its own engine works and was described as "the most complete in Britain, excepting those of the Crown."

Outstanding among Scott's products during the middle years of the nineteenth century were the vessels *HMS Greenock* and the Blue Funnel liner *Agamemnon*. The former owes its uniqueness to the fact that she was screw propelled and built of iron, which was almost unknown in 1849. The *Agamemnon*, launched in 1865, was unusually large for her time and was a direct attempt to put an end to the monopoly of sailing ships on the Far Eastern routes by producing a steamship capable of carrying an economic cargo and having bunkers which could carry sufficient supplies of coal for long voyages. This and the rapid advances made in marine engineering guaranteed the success of the *Agamemnon* and her sister ships, *Ajax* and *Achilles*. These were the first ships to be fitted with compound engines.

Scott's had a special relationship with the Admiralty built up over many years and in both World Wars the bulk of the yard's output was for this source. In 1909 and 1912 the Dreadnoughts *Colossus* and *Ajax* were constructed at Scott's and the world's first steam submarine, the S1, was also built there. In the inter-war years Scott's produced the diesel-electric oil tanker *Brunswick* which was the first tanker built on the Clyde to have the super-structure placed aft. After the Second World War the yard embarked on contracts of various kinds ranging from passenger/cargo liners for the Far East to bulk carriers, general purpose cargo vessels and naval frigates. The company enjoyed good relations with the Union-Castle and Clan Lines and built a substantial number of ships for both fleets.

Following the findings of the Geddes Committee in 1966 the decision was taken to merge this great yard with Lithgows Limited and the following year Scott-Lithgow Limited was formed.

Robert Napier and Sons

David and Robert Napier were cousins born within a year of each other in the early 1790's. David was the outstanding engineer in the family but he lacked the entrepreneurial flair needed to sell the products of his genius. Robert on the other hand was a born

15

salesman as well as being an engineer of considerable ability. These factors, coupled with an obsessive determination to produce only goods of exceptional quality, were to make him the uncrowned king of Clyde shipbuilding.

In 1821 he leased the Calmachie engine works from David Napier and within two years had manufactured his first effective marine engine for the paddle steamer *Leven*. By 1830 he had purchased the Vulcan Foundry in Washington Street, Glasgow and converted it into a marine engineering works. The high point of this period came in 1835 when he was asked by the East India Company to engine their newest ship *Berenice*. This was Robert's first attempt at constructing an ocean-going marine engine and was so successful that he was awarded the Admiralty contract for the building of two warships, the *Vesuvius* and the *Stromboli* in 1837. A year earlier he had taken over cousin David's Lancefield site, which was his base for the next five years, and in 1838 he produced the machinery for the trans-Atlantic vessel *British Queen*. By this time he was heavily involved with Samuel Cunard, whose vision of a fleet of mail-carrying steam packets working to a regular timetable held great appeal for the engineer. Napier subscribed some £6000 to the venture and was to recruit many more investors to help make up the £270,000 needed to get the project off the ground. His reward for such dedicated support was the contract to build and engine the first four trans-Atlantic vessels for the British and North American Royal Mail Steam Navigation Company, or Cunard as it became better known.

Napier was a marine engineer not a shipbuilder and in order to fulfil his contractual obligations was forced to allocate the building of the hulls to the firms of John Wood and Richard Steele on the lower Clyde. In 1840 he purchased the Govan Old Yard to be able to construct iron steamships in his own right. The yard opened the following year and its first vessel, *PS Vanguard*, was launched in 1843. Thereafter contracts poured in, so much so that Napier required larger premises. The firm moved in 1850 to Govan East Shipyard and there it remained until the turn of the century.

Robert Napier retired in 1860 handing over control to his two sons but their commitment to shipbuilding was not nearly so strong.

By the 1870's the yard was in decline and upon Robert's death in 1876 the business was sold to a group headed by A C Kirk, formerly one of Napier's apprentices. Kirk had made his mark as designer of an early triple expansion engine which was installed in the *Propontis*, a cargo liner built by John Elder's firm. Under his chairmanship the Napier yard flourished. In 1886 it built the *Aberdeen* for the Aberdeen Line, whose triple expansion engine design was to dominate marine engineering for the next twenty years, and in 1891 the beautiful *Ophir* was constructed for the Orient Line. Kirk died in 1892 and the company was bought over by William Beardmore and Sons who moved its base of operation to Dalmuir, thus removing from the shipbuilding scene the name of one of its greatest pioneers.

Alexander Stephen and Sons

Stephen's enjoyed a long and eventful history in the shipbuilding trade spanning well over one hundred years, although the family's involvement with ship construction pre-dated the setting up of the firm by nearly eighty years. Alexander Stephen started his shipbuilding career in 1750 at Burghead near Lossiemouth. His nephew, William, soon followed him into the business and worked there for ten years before opening his own yard in Aberdeen in 1793. A further yard was opened in turn by his son, also called William, at Arbroath in 1814 but this venture, together with the Aberdeen yard, collapsed in 1828.

William's brother, Alexander, then stepped in and took over all the shipbuilding interests, operating under the name Alexander Stephen and Son. The business moved to Dundee in 1843 but early in 1851 the centre of operations was shifted to Kelvinhaugh in Glasgow, although the Dundee yard continued to function. Ships were built and repaired at Kelvinhaugh for nearly twenty years before the firm transferred to its final site at Linthouse in 1870. From then until the demise of the company 547 vessels were constructed, all of the highest quality.

The yard established its own engine works in 1871 thereby reducing the need to 'buy-in' machinery and from then on specialised in the building of cargo-passenger vessels. Their most notable product was the early turbine steamship *Virginian* built for the Allan

Line in 1904. However, their most elegant ships were produced for the Elders and Fyffes and the Imperial Direct West Indian Line for the transportation of bananas and a limited number of passengers. While rarely in the forefront of design or technological innovation Stephen's maintained the highest standards and carefully vetted all aspects of design, especially from a commercial point of view. Such considerations led P & O to place orders there for three important vessels in the late 20's-the magnificent turbo-electric *Viceroy of India*, the *Corfu* and the *Carthage*. Contracts of a diverse nature for the Royal Navy were a regular source of income. These included the fast minelayer *Manxman*, capable of speeds up to 38 knots, the aircraft carrier *Ocean* of 1945 and the famous *Amethyst*, a sloop which earned its place in maritime history by making a dash in 1949 from the Chinese Communist forces down the River Yangtse and subsequently starred in a film of her exploits.

The yard ceased to function independently in 1968 having become a member of the UCS Consortium, but it will always be remembered as a good and respected employer. Although the old yard now lies silent one tangible element has been preserved for posterity. Stephen's Engineering works, originally part of the Glasgow Exhibition of 1888 in Kelvingrove has been re-assembled as a working exhibit at the Scottish Maritime Museum in Irvine.

William Denny and Brothers

William Denny built the *Margery*, the first steamer to operate on the River Thames in 1814 but it was his sons who founded the Dumbarton firm of William Denny and Brothers in 1845. They could not have known when they launched their first vessel, the *PS Loch Lomond*, that the company would become a world-wide influence on almost every aspect of ship construction and design. From the very beginning the Denny brothers encouraged training and technical development which raised draughtsmanship to an art. In 1884 the company issued its *Code of Procedure*, which laid down the requirements for the smooth running of all departments within the yard. All features of ship performance were carefully recorded including measured time trials, fuel consumption, hull resistance and so on. The firm commenced operations as shipbuliders but later became marine engineers as well, trading under the name of Tulloch and Denny, later Denny and Company. Their engine works provided Cunard and P & O with the first compound engines in the 1860's.

Highly ranked among the company's many achievements were the construction of the *Rotomahana* in 1878, the first all-steel merchant ship, and the *King Edward* in 1901, the world's first turbine passenger steamer. The latter was held in special affection by Glasgow's "doon the watter" travelling public and although scrapped in 1950 her engines were preserved to form part of the collection at the Glasgow Museum of Transport. Perhaps not so well known was the close relationship the yard had with institutions such as Glasgow University, the city's Royal Technical College (now Strathclyde University) and the Massachusetts Institute of Technology, in some cases providing these with lecturers and department heads. The company also offered university scholarships and extensive patronage to the burgh of Dumbarton. Employees were treated as members of the family something which the firm's directors carried over into the boardroom; throughout its life Denny's stayed in the family's hands. The firm was held in high esteem and it established long relationships with many companies including British India, P & O, Union Steamship Company, Patrick Henderson (which had Denny directors on its board) and the Irrawady Flotilla.

Other famous vessels launched from the yard included the Scot (1890) for the Union Steamship Company, the *TS Victoria* (1953) for the Irish service and *Shamrock II*, an America's Cup challenger built for the tea magnate Sir Thomas Lipton.

Fairfield Shipbuilding and Engineering Company

In 1864 a new shipyard was laid out by John Elder at Fairfield near Govan and began operating four years later under the trade name John Elder and Company. Elder's involvement with maritime affairs dated back to 1852 when he made a name for himself as a partner in the marine engineering firm of Randolph, Elder and Company. As with the Thomsons, he too had worked for Robert Napier before branching out on his own. The yard's facilities were extended in 1868 and work started on the construction of a new engine and boiler works, although this was not completed until 1874. Upon Elder's death in 1869 the firm was reorganised under a new Managing Director, Sir William Pearce, and from then on was to achieve a reputation for building some of the most technically advanced ships of the time. These included the Cunarder *Oregon* (1883), the *Umbria* and *Etruria* (1884-85) and the superliners *Campania* and *Lucania* (1893), all holders of the coveted Blue Riband for the fastest crossing of the North Atlantic. In 1885 the firm was radically restructured and changed its name to the Fairfield Shipbuilding and Engineering Company.

After the death of Sir William Pearce in 1888 the Managing Directorship passed to his son Sir W G Pearce and the yard continued to maintain the highest standards with continuous investment in plant and machinery. A feature of the yard was its speed of construction. One example of this was the Caledonian Steam Packet Company's *Duchess of Fife*, a coastal passenger paddle steamer which was laid down on 17th January 1903, launched on 9th May and completed her trials on 5th June. Fairfield's reputation for quality ensured that it enjoyed strong links with the CPR and Union-Castle Lines and helped to win a number of lucrative Admiralty contracts. However, the limited berthing facilities at Govan prevented the firm tendering for the large liners of the twentieth century, most of which were built at John Brown's in Clydebank.

In 1907, after the death of Sir W G Pearce, the company passed under the control of a consortium. This group continued to operate the business until it collapsed in the mid-twenties leaving the yard to soldier on alone. Despite a slight improvement in the shipbuilding market in 1935, Fairfield was struck another blow when the Anchor Line folded. The bankrupt shipping line could not meet its debts to the shipyard which was now on the point of collapse. Fortunately the Lithgow Group stepped in to purchase Fairfield as a going concern and this relationship lasted for the next thirty years.

John Brown and Company

The Clydebank yard was the best known, if for no other reason than that the *Queen Mary* and her sister *Queen Elizabeth* were built there. Its origins lay in a small engineering firm established by the brothers James and George Thomson at Finnieston in 1847. They began with the construction of marine engines and quickly established a reputation for quality and reliability. The progression to shipbuilding was made in 1851 when the Thomsons opened a shipyard at Cessnock Bank in Govan, specialising in the passenger vessel market. Both men had learned their skills at Robert Napier's yard in the 1840's and this apprenticeship was to pay off handsomely. Their most significant ship of this period was the Cunard record breaker *Russia*, built in 1867. Four years later the decision was taken to move to Clydebank which offered the opportunity to lay out the yard properly and set up good engine building facilities. The *Servia*, a single-screw steamship, was built for Cunard in 1881 and was second in size only to Isambard Kingdom Brunel's *Great Eastern*. Later in the decade the yard completed contracts for the Inman Line, producing in the *City of New York* and the *City of Paris* (1888) two of the most beautiful vessels of all time.

The nineties were bad years in which the company made major losses. Drastic restructuring was necessary and as a result the Thomsons lost control in 1897. The new management struggled on for another two years but was powerless to prevent a take-over bid by John Brown and Company, the Sheffield steelmakers, from being successful. Brown's was the country's main supplier of armour plating and had been looking for new outlets for their products for some time; the Clydebank shipyard was ideal. The new owners embarked on a policy of rapid modernisation and, despite being controlled from south of the border, the shipyard retained almost unrestricted autonomy. It was largely as a result of the reorganisation of the 1890's that the company won the order to build the *Lusitania*, which the Government and Cunard had originally marked for Barrow.

From 1899 till 1968 nearly 400 vessels were launched from this great yard. These are just a few of the most notable: *Caronia* (1905), *Lusitania* (1906), *Aquitania* (1913), *HMS Hood* (1920),*HMS Vanguard* (1946), *Queen Mary* (1934) *Queen Elizabeth* (1938) and *QE2* (1967).

Yarrow and Company

This firm was originally established in 1865 on the River Thames by Alfred Fernandez Yarrow. In the early years it concentrated on building steam launches before specialising in the construction of shallow draught ships and torpedo-boats. It was with the latter that the company really began to make its name, launching Torpedo Boat No 14 for the Royal Navy in 1878. Yarrow then went on to produce a series of naval vessels which counteracted the effectiveness of such ships; these were the world's first destroyers *HMS Havock* and *HMS Hornet*. In 1906 the firm moved to its present site at Scotstoun largely on account of the availability of high quality steel and a willingness on the part of the local workforce to accept lower wages than their English counterparts.

The yard's reputation rests entirely on its ability to construct light naval craft, which it supplied not only to the Admiralty but to the navies of Spain, Russia and Japan among others. One important product of the early years at Scotstoun was *HMS Lurcher* (1911) which had a remarkable top speed of 35 knots and was a fore-runner of the modern destroyer. After the Second World War company designers were responsible for producing ships for anti-aircraft and anti-submarine work as well as general purpose vessels which had a role to play within NATO; the Rothesay and Leander Classes and the Types 21 and 22 frigates were Yarrow products. The Type 22's were of special note, coming into service just before the Falklands War. *HMS Broadsword* was the first of the class and was fitted with twin screw gas turbines giving her a maximum speed of over 30 knots. From 1945 Yarrow followed a policy of varied ship construction which included RNLI lifeboats, ferries for African lakes and rivers and even trawlers, but in recent years the yard has produced mainly for the Admiralty and the navies of other countries. Over 400 vessels have been completed by the company since it moved to Scotstoun at the turn of the century.

Parts of the firm were nationalised in the late 1960's thus creating Yarrow Shipbuilders Ltd but Yarrow & Co, the original holding company, remained independent. Today it controls Y-ARD Ltd, a firm of consultants which has built up an international reputation specialising in matters of defence, engineering and naval architecture.

WORKING IN THE SHIPYARDS

Shipyard workers endured a tough existence for what was often a mere pittance of a wage. Yet, they were fiercely proud of the work they did and the vessels they created. Inter-yard rivalry was commonplace and great store was put on company loyalty. Fairfield's drew most of their workforce from Govan, Brown's from Clydebank and Denny from Dumbarton. Interlopers were rarely made welcome. A Glasgow joiner who had just started at the Denny yard asked one of his new workmates for directions to the firm's general store; the man replied that he had no idea as he was new to the yard himself. It later transpired that this man had worked at Denny's for fifteen years!

Dangers

The completion of contracts on time was of paramount importance to the shipbuilders for fear of incurring penalties for late delivery. This invariably meant working in all weathers. Although in later years the yards adopted a more benevolent attitude to their workforce, the late nineteenth and early twentieth centuries were much less enlightened. Winter was worst. Accident rates were high and in low temperatures it was not unknown for men to suffer frostbite when handling ice-cold steel. The most common accidents were falls. Heavy rains followed by severe frosts could turn steel hulls into walls of ice and decks into skating rinks. Injuries caused by crushing were also frequent. Yet, the yards offered only the most primitive medical facilities and until comparatively recently the victims and their families received little or no compensation for industrial injuries.

The worst disaster in the history of Clyde shipbuilding happened at the yard of Alexander Stephen on Tuesday 3rd July 1883. That day, the small steam coaster *Daphne* was due to be launched. She had been ordered for the Glasgow, Dublin and Londonderry Steam Packet Company's Irish and Scottish Coastal Services. Stephen's had built up a reputation for carefully planned and prepared launches, but until this time little attention was paid by builders to matters of vertical stability or to the capability of a hull to meet its requirements. It was assumed that the naval architects and their clients possessed the specialist knowledge to tackle such problems. Work on the *Daphne* was well advanced, but as the shipyard did not have a fitting out quay the ship's two cylinder compound engine was installed prior to launching with a gaping hole left on the deck for the fitting of her boilers at a later date. Some two hundred men remained on board during the launch so that work could progress steadily. After the naming ceremony the *Daphne* slid slowly into the Clyde. Seconds later she suddenly heeled to port, hung there momentarily, then rolled over completely. The disaster claimed 124 lives.

An enquiry revealed that the capsize was speeded up by some thirty tons of loose gear careering across the *Daphne's* open deck, by the sheer weight of two hundred men sliding across to the port side and by the water entering the boiler access hole when the ship plunged beneath the water level. The disaster was more attributable to design errors of the ship than to Stephen's launch procedures, but the results of the tragic affair were manifold. In future, ships would have their positions of centre of gravity estimated before launch; all weights aboard would be firmly secured; the numbers of personnel aboard a ship limited to only those needed to moor the vessel once launched or to carry out a post-launch examination. As for the bereaved, their only assistance came from the moneys raised by public subscription.

Wages and Lay-offs

Wage levels in the industry were a frequent source of workers' grievance. By the mid-1950's a shipyard worker's pay packet was on average around £8 15/- per week, four times the level of the Depression years, with a top wage of around £10. Basic wages could be supplemented by overtime and indeed for most workers this was the only way to make 'real money'. For new entrants to the yards earnings were more meagre still. In the late 1940's apprentices at Yarrows started work with a weekly wage of 18/6d and this would rise only gradually over the next five years until they qualified as skilled tradesmen. A generation earlier, c1928, a plater's boy could expect to earn around 8/11d per week rising after several years to a top line of £2 15/-, if he learned a trade. In some yards a bonus was paid, anything between 2/6d and 5/-, each time a ship was launched.

Another contentious issue for shipyard trade unions was the casual nature of the work itself. With the exception of key personnel the yards tended to hire and fire at will. After the Second World War it was not unknown for hundreds, and sometimes thousands, of carpenters, joiners, platers, boilermen, shipwrights, plumbers and painters to be summoned by the yard foremen and given two hours notice of redundancy. By the mid-sixties the unions had succeeded in making a Friday the only day when such action could be taken, thus ensuring at least a full week's pay for the workforce. Of course misconduct could mean instant dismissal and, in pre-war years, even minor misdemeanours could bring a fine. Employees caught 'brewing up' for example, could be punished for taking an illegal tea break-there weren't any legal ones-although the money was returned to the guilty party if he left the yard.

In the forties and fifties lay-offs presented few problems to a workforce whose skills could be utilised by other yards or industries, but in the twenties and thirties unemployment brought acute deprivation and near starvation for some families. When work stopped on Hull 534 in 1931, John Brown and Company were forced to make some 3,000 men redundant and this had the knock-on effect of creating a further 7,000 more unemployed in the various sub-contracting and ancillary industries. Whole families were forced into subsistence living with little assistance from the state. Unemployment benefit was paid at 15/- per week for a man, 12/6d for a woman, 7/6d for a boy and 6/6d for a girl. 'Unemployment benefit is not a living wage; it was never meant to be that', declared Ramsay MacDonald in justification of the harsh economy measures of 1931, which included the hated means test; many who had worked, paid unemployment insurance and saved, were forced to rely on the Parish Councils for help. Potatoes, bread, dripping and jam became the staple diet of the ever-increasing ranks of unemployed, although some found temporary relief by persuading trawlermen using the Forth and Clyde Canal to part with the odd box of herring which would provide a decent meal for at least two or three days in the week. The high incidence of rickets among the children of shipyard workers at this time was directly attributable to poor living conditions and the lack of a healthy diet.

In such times a sense of humour helped keep the soul if not the body alive. An American, who was standing looking up at the deserted hull of the *Queen Mary* some twenty months after work had stopped, said to his companions "Look at all that rust on her shell", to which an unemployed local retorted "Ye should come up an' see ma frying pan!". On another occasion a group of out-of-work platers were passing the time of day on a Clydebank street when one lad reported, "Ah heard a chap got a start up in Aberdeen!"

Working Conditions

Working conditions were spartan in most shipyards, though some yards were known to be worse than others. Until the late 1950's or early 60's there were no mid-morning tea breaks and, before the war, no canteens either. The hours worked varied only slightly from yard to yard and changed little over fifty years or so. Most employees clocked on around 7.45am and worked through till 12.15pm; there was an hour off for lunch and the day's work finished around 5.45pm. Saturday mornings were used on occasion to complete a vessel or where construction was behind schedule. In total this meant a working week of between 45 and 48 hours. Overtime, which was frequently available, could be as much as four hours per day.

Some yards, Yarrows for instance, insisted that apprentices supplied their own tools on taking up employment while others, like Brown's, practised a system of 'bonding'. This allowed an apprentice to be supplied by the yard with tools which he was permitted to keep once he had served his time. This practice, which was open to exploitation, was ended in the late 50's. Under the 'bonding' system a trainee who changed yards before completing his apprenticeship would forfeit any claim to his tools-this also applied to anyone who went out on strike. Subsequently it became common practice for apprentices to put by some of their wages in order to buy the tools required.

Little attention was paid to health and safety in the pre-war days but things improved considerably in the 1950's. Most yards had an ambulance room, an ambulance on stand by, at least one resident nurse, a visiting doctor and periodic physical check-ups for every employee. There was compensation for serious industrial injury but for minor scrapes or ailments incurred through work only sick pay was given and this was not commensurate with wages. Many yards worked a system of Mutual Aid where workers paid in around 6d per week and this could be used to supplement sick benefit if needed. There was also a Death Benefit Fund where a grant of £50 was given to bereaved families. This was administered by a Yard Committee made up of members of each department.

One aspect of health of great concern to all employees was the provision of toilet facilities. In some yards these were primitive to say the least. Before going to the toilet a worker had to report to his foreman and present his clocking-in disc, usually a brass disc with an individual's works number stamped on it. He then had seven minutes to complete his ablutions and return the disc upon pain of having his wages docked if late. A few of the older yards retained toilets fitted with a curved steel-spiked bar attached to the pipe connecting the bowl to the cistern, as a deterrent to would-be laggards. The same effect was achieved by apprentices who threw water-filled bags over the top of occupied cubicles.

Yard hierarchy could be a complicated affair with some variation from firm to firm. All were bureaucratic in structure with clearly defined systems of accountability and routes of communication. Every man, in theory, knew to whom he was responsible and detailed job descriptions gave him a clear idea of what was expected of him. A general outline of the management structure is given below.

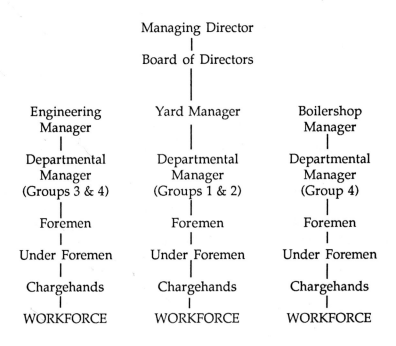

GROUP 1: Finishing Trades   Joiners shop, electrical supplies, plumbers, painters, carpenters, riggers, upholsterers

GROUP 2: Black Squads   Blacksmiths, angle-iron smiths, sheet-iron workers, copper-smiths, platers, shipwrights, welders, loftsmen

GROUP 3: Fabricating Engines   Turners, fitters, engineers, brass finishers

GROUP 4: Boilershops   Pressers, boilermakers, welders, platers, caulkers

One sight now lost to Glasgow is that of thousands of men streaming from the yard gates at the end of the working day. The major yards operated tacit agreements with each other over starting and finishing times, which were staggered to allow the public

DINNER HOUR, JOHN BROWN AND Co. SHIPBUILDING YARD, CLYDEBANK

transport system to cope with this surging mass of humanity. Clydebank was the first to open in the morning and the first to close at night. Further up the river each yard opened or closed five or ten minutes after its neighbour. William Denny's was the exception to this rule, being rather isolated from the rest and Dumbarton's principal employer. At one point the management there had been concerned about a spate of break-ins and decided, among other measures, to have the gates topped with barbed wire. They entrusted the job to a joiner of questionable intellect, suspect skill and doubtful sobriety. No one thought to check his work though its failings became all too apparent when the hooter sounded at the end of the day. As the weary mob lumbered towards the gates they failed to open. The barbed wire had been strung right across the top with no means of parting it where the gates met. It took a further fifteen minutes to obtain a pair of wire cutters and release the irate workforce.

HULL 534, THE QUEEN MARY

Idleness and Rust

For twenty-seven months Hull 534 lay rusting on the stocks at John Brown's yard in Clydebank, a victim of the depression which followed the crash on the US Stock Exchange in October 1929. Cunard, desperately short of capital to complete Britain's first one thousand foot liner, reluctantly suspended further work on the ship, forcing the shipyard to make sweeping redundancies. By December 1931 two thirds of Brown's workforce had been laid-off leaving the unfinished liner, a symbol of economic disaster, to dominate the Clydebank skyline.

Work was resumed again in April 1934, a tribute to the energetic efforts of David Kirkwood, Labour Member of Parliament for the Dumbarton Burghs. Time after time he brought the plight of the unemployed in his constituency to the attention of the House of Commons:

"I believe that as long as No 534 lies like a skeleton in my constituency so long will the depression last in this country. To me it seems to shout 'Failure! Failure!' to the whole of Britain."

CUNARD WHIE STAR LINER, "534" — THE WORLD'S LARGEST LINER.
Launched at Clydebank and Christened by Her Majesty The Queen, 26th Sept. 1934.

Finally the government relented and agreed to make Cunard a repayable loan on condition they took over the ailing White Star Line whose fortunes had slumped badly during the late twenties and early thirties. Reluctantly Cunard agreed and a new company, Cunard-White Star, was created with a grant of £9.5 million: £3 million for the 534; £5 million for a projected sister ship and £1.5 million to provide working capital for the new company. The Clydebank folk were ecstatic. For over a month 400 men worked on the hull removing 130 tons of rust and on 26th May 1934 formal notice was given to restart construction.

Dimensions

The volume of materials consumed in the construction of any liner could reach enormous proportions. In the case of the *Queen Mary* the figures were confounding: 10,000,000 rivets, 4,000 miles of electric cables, 30,000 lamps, 70,000 gallons of paint, 6 miles of carpet...No effort was spared to make this the wonder ship of the age and everything about her was massive:

80,000 tons gross;
Over 1000 feet in length;
12 decks;
A hull of 35,000 tons divided into 160 watertight compartments;
Four sets of quadruple expansion, reduced geared turbines developing 50,000 Horsepower;
7 turbo-generators supplied 10,000 kilowatts of power to light 30,000 electric bulbs, operate 22 lifts and 596 clocks;
4 propellers, 20 feet in diameter, each weighing 35 tons;
3 whistles, 6' 7"long, each weighing over a ton

The art-deco interiors of the Queen Mary were a radical departure from anything seen before on a British ship. Bulkheads and pillars were veneered in over fifty types of wood. Thirty-six artists, among them Kenneth Shoesmith, C Cameron Baillie, Edward Wadsworth and MacDonald Gill, contributed works to adorn the staterooms, public rooms and galleries. One of the most popular paintings hung in the Tourist Class Smoking Room. This depicted the old *Mauretania* in cruising white, streaked with rust and smoke belching from her stacks en route to the breakers yard at Rosyth in 1935.

The ship boasted a children's playroom, a library, drawing rooms, galleries, shops, smoking rooms, lounges, a ballroom, an observation lounge, squash courts, swimming pools, Turkish baths, a health studio, hairdressing salon, restaurants and the world's first floating synagogue! Some rooms were enormous. The Cabin Class Restaurant measured 143 feet long, 118 feet wide and had a height of 27 feet, making it just about the largest room afloat.

LAUNCH OF CUNARD WHITE STAR LINER "QUEEN MARY" BY H.M. THE QUEEN AT CLYDEBANK, SEPTEMBER 26th, 1934 *(Central Press)*

Until the day of the launch the giant ship was known to the public only by her shipyard number 534. There are two stories about the choice of name, at least one of which is true. Legend has it that Cunard originally intended to name her *Victoria*. Accordingly Lord Royden, a Cunard director and personal friend of George V, approached the King and asked if he would give permission for the new liner to be named after England's(sic) most illustrious and remarkable Queen. The King took this to be the greatest compliment ever paid to his wife and enthusiastically agreed to ask her; so *Queen Mary* it was. True story or not the name was a suitable one as it avoided any fractious argument over whether the Cunard or White Star tradition of name-endings, 'ia' and 'ic' respectively, should be upheld. Before the name could be publicly revealed however, a further complication had to be resolved; there was a Clyde steamer already in service called *Queen Mary*. The owners, Williamson Buchanan Steamers Ltd, eventually agreed to call their vessel *Queen Mary II* and allow Cunard to use the original name for what had become the national flagship. In gratitude, Cunard presented a plaque and a portrait of Queen Mary which were proudly displayed in the steamer's lounge.

The Launch

There is a certain poignancy about the launch of a great ship. It is the moment when an inert mass of steel leaves the place of its birth and takes on a life of its own. During the golden age of Clyde Shipbuilding a launch always generated great excitement among shipyard workers and within the local community. For an important vessel the launching ceremony assumed the nature of a full-dress display with distinguished lady guest on hand to perform the christening, press the launch button and shatter the traditional bottle of champagne across the ship's bows. Local residents transformed the event into a gala day: shops closed early; windows were decorated; children were given a day off school; everyone vied with each other for the best spot to observe the launch and afterwards the local pubs were filled to capacity with well-wishers and an air of self-congratulation. Sadly, such scenes are now a thing of the past and it is difficult for those who have never witnessed a great ship take to the water for the first time to appreciate what an emotional moment it can be. This was especially true of the long-awaited launch of the *Queen Mary*.

On a cold, wet and windy Wednesday 26th September 1934, the great ship, her hull supported by piles and her bow and stern cradled on the fore and after poppets, stood on the greased standing ways at John Brown's. In due course the keelblocks would be removed and the restraining triggers, which held the ship on the ways, released; 2,350 tons of drag chains would check her rapid progress into the Clyde.

Queen Mary had graciously agreed to perform the launching ceremony, the first time a British monarch had ever done so. A special glass-fronted platform had been erected for the royal party and yard officials nervously awaited their arrival. For the

BBC this was to be one of their most ambitious broadcasts-an international occasion beamed at the nations of the Empire. US networks and European companies also proposed to relay the BBC broadcast. It was known that the King would accompany Queen Mary so the BBC engineers devised a simple early warning system. A royal drive would take just minutes from Scotstounhill post office to the gate at John Brown's. An open telephone line was arranged from the post office to the BBC's control room so that when the King and Queen drove past the postmistress would inform broadcasting officials with the words "The King is passing". This was announcer George Blake's cue to start his commentary. Thereafter everything went to plan.

From behind the rain-streaked windows of the platform the Queen made her first ever public speech:

"I am happy to name this ship *Queen Mary*. I wish
success to her and all who sail in her"

She then cut the pink ribbon holding not champagne, but a bottle of Australian wine. It cascaded over the liner's knife-edged bow whereupon the Queen turned to her husband and asked, "Was that right?"

CABIN STARBOARD GALLERY

37

A loud crash signalled the release of the triggers and seconds later six powerful hydraulic rams began to push the hull in the direction of the river. As the ship gained momentum the bundles of drag chains attached to various points along the hull suddenly began to move, creating an almighty din and enveloping spectators in dense, choking clouds of rust. The cheering reached a crescendo as the *Queen Mary* made her stately entry into the Clyde. Spectators lining the opposite shore were swamped by the flood-wave set in motion by the displacement of thousands of tons of water. Within a hundred seconds the launch was complete and tugs were pushing and pulling the giant towards her fitting out basin. The royal party left the scene but at the end of the jetty stood Jimmy Reid, the yard foreman, gazing at the newly launched *Queen Mary*. He seemed to be muttering something to himself but the words were carried in the wind and picked up by a BBC official who later repeated them:

"Aye, she's no the *Rex*, and she's no the *Bremen*, and she's no the *Normandie*, but she's bluidy well oor idea o' a ship"

When fitting out was completed and her trials under way the Cunard publicity machine went into action. The *Queen Mary* starred in a documentary film entitled *Wonder Ship*. Posters, cigarette cards, postcards and other souvenirs were widely available. One of the most enduring cards featured the *Queen Mary* straddling Trafalgar Square conveying an impression of her great size. Others showed the ship's length measured against landmarks like the Eiffel Tower and the Empire State Building or three express locomotives in line abreast coming thundering out of her funnels. There were Queen Mary tea-towels, table cloths, head squares, biscuit and bon-bon tins, books and even records, one of which began:

We're happy and gay,
Cos' we're on our way,
We've booked our trip to the USA,
On the greatest ship on the sea,
The Queen Mary's for me...

However, as Cunard had secured the services of Henry Hall and the BBC Dance Orchestra for the maiden voyage it was not altogether surprising that the official theme song of *RMS Queen Mary* was *Somewhere at Sea* which Hall had composed specially for this momentous event. For four nights the band broadcast from the ship to a rapturous radio audience in Britain. This was in itself a significant technological achievement.

FIRST SAILING of R.M.S. "QUEEN MARY"
from **SOUTHAMPTON**
WEDNESDAY, 27th MAY

COMBINED RAIL & SEAT TICKETS ... **10/6**

COMBINED RAIL & STEAMER TICKETS ... **25/-**

BOOKINGS ALSO FROM CERTAIN SUBURBAN STATIONS

TICKETS STRICTLY LIMITED
BOOK IN ADVANCE AT STATIONS

Ask for handbill giving full details at S.R. Stations.

SOUTHERN RAILWAYS SOUTHAMPTON DOCKS

Liner of the Age ?

Not everyone gloried in Clydebank's achievement. The *Architect and Building News* was of the opinion that the *Queen Mary's* internal appointments were "mild but expensive vulgarity". There was considerable criticism of the ship's pseudo-Gothic style and uninspired art-deco design, somewhat reminiscent of an Odeon Cinema. Comparison with the French *Normandie*, a vessel described by A C Hardie of the *Times* as "the most remarkable and luxurious liner of this epoch", was inevitable. German marine engineers were of the opinion that her design was "nicht verbesserungsfahig", unimprovable, but the British stayed loyal to the *Queen Mary*. Two young stockbrokers managed to secure tourist class tickets for the maiden voyage in late May 1936 and were eagerly boasting of their good luck to fellow brokers. An older colleague butted in exclaiming, "Surely you're not travelling with Cunard." Taken rather aback one of the two replied falteringly, "Yes". "Personally I always sail with the French Line" retorted the older man. "But haven't the French ships got a reputation for bad time-keeping, poor service and a lack of cleanliness?" asked the young broker. "Hell, yes" came the reply, "but at least there's none of this bloody rubbish about women and children first!"

Perhaps the passenger who, when discussing the relative merits of the *Mary* and her rival with Captain Thoreux of the *Normandie*, came closest to the truth when she said, "In my opinion, the *Queen Mary* is a grand Englishwoman in sportsgear - the *Normandie* is a very gay French girl in evening dress."

The *Queen Mary's* rivals *Normandie* (top), *Bremen* (left). *Rex* (right)

Whatever one believes, the *Queen Mary* appeared at a time when national prestige was badly flagging. She became a symbol of British maritime pride which had taken such a severe knock after the German liners *Bremen* and *Europa* had wrested the Blue Riband

40

from the old *Mauritania* in 1929, only to lose it to Italy's *Rex* and the French *Normandie* in turn. When the *Mary* finally won the trophy against all opposition in 1938 she held on to it for the next fourteen years until the *United States* eclipsed everything on the Atlantic in 1952, a record which is still unbroken. Passengers looked on the *Queen Mary* with affection for she was a happy ship earning for herself a loyal, admiring clientelle.

Although no longer in service the *Queen Mary* survives as a glowing tribute to marine technology and the shipbuilder's art.

Drawing by Alan McKay

CLYDE BUILT

Elegance and Power

In the first decade of the twentieth century sail was still common sight on the high seas. The steamships of the period retained such sailing ship features as tall pole masts carrying sail, clipper stems, elliptical sterns and rake and sheer owing more than a little to the windjammers of the late 1890's. Steamships tended to conform to a limited pattern of hull design and deckhouse configuration but there the similarity ended. Liners operating on the prestigious North Atlantic routes, where competition was cutthroat, offered an extravagant luxury to first class passengers unequalled elsewhere. At the other end of the spectrum were the emigrant carriers of spartan simplicity. Ships on other world wide routes compared at best with the intermediate liners commuting between British and American ports.

The designing of an ocean liner was a large and complex task requiring the combined efforts of naval architects, marine engineers, interior designers and artists. If their efforts harmonised the finished product was acclaimed as a triumph of aesthetic and technological enterprise while failure to please public taste could well doom a ship's chances of commercial success. Some of the ideas incorporated in successive new designs evolved through logical progression in the search for improved efficiency and performance, for example, the change from coal burning to oil firing which gained momentum in the 1920's. Others owed more to the ever-changing trends in fashion.

Profiles
In the period leading up to World War One deckhouses and superstructures began to be grouped together, an important departure from the sailing ship which, for reasons of stability, had no formal superstructure. Old style pole masts were replaced by king posts which improved cargo handling. In the aftermath of the *Titanic* disaster in 1912 greater numbers of lifeboats were carried and advances made in the design of davits and other life-saving equipment. Liner profiles were radically altered in the years fol-

lowing 1918: cruiser sterns were adopted to improve stability and provide extra passenger space; the number of masts carried reduced to one or two, although some fleets like the Bibby Line continued to have four masts on their vessels right up until World War Two; in the late twenties the fashion for low squat funnels appeared and they were fewer in number (Germany's twin liners *Bremen* and *Europa* were among the first to adopt this style). The turn of the century had seen the introduction of 'four stackers'. On German ships these were arranged in pairs but on British ships such as the *Olympic* and the *Titanic* the funnels were spaced equally. There was no need for this proliferation and in most cases at least one was a dummy. However, if tall and well-raked, as was the case with the White Star sisters, they looked impressive and conveyed a strong impression of power which proved immensely popular, particularly with the emigrant trade. In the inter-war years the funnel served either as an exhaust for smoke and fumes from the boiler uptakes or as an additional storage facility. The French liner *Normandie* had three funnels, one of which contained a childrens' playroom and florist shop while another functioned as a kennel for the passengers' pets!

Machinery

One of the most important developments in marine engineering after the First World War was the general acceptance of the turbine engine. Earlier ships had simple steam engines of low horsepower, usually driving paddles. Fuel consumption was high and so journeys were necessarily short. The two cylinder engine evolved from this only to be superseded by the triple expansion engine which, although slow, was economic and reliable. Steam was generated in Scotch fire-tube boilers, passed through a small high pressure cylinder to a medium-sized one and finally to a low pressure cylinder which was the largest of the three. Collectively these types of machinery were known as steam reciprocating engines. The turbine was a great improvement on all of these for it sprayed steam, generated in water-tube boilers, at very high pressure onto small blades on the rim of a cylinder forcing the shaft to rotate at around 4,000rpm. At first the turbine could be used only in very fast vessels but its application widened when systems of single and double reduction gearing were developed as these had the effect of reducing the number of revs to around 100rpm. The marine engine took a further step forward with the introduction of diesels, first pioneered on Denmark's *Selandia* of 1912, although for many years these were used only on cargo ships and intermediate sized liners such as the last White Star sisters *Georgic* and *Britannic*. Today diesels have largely taken over from the steam turbine but they represent only one of the alternative power sources available to ship owners. Gas turbines, electric propulsion and even nuclear power have been used in vessels before, offering varying degrees of efficiency and economy.

End of an Age

The inter-war years saw the rise of the cruising market and the introduction of purpose built vessels fitted with air-conditioning and having hulls of reduced size and draught capable of negotiating shallow water ports. Cruising has remained popular to the present day and accounts for a substantial part of passenger-carrying shipping. It has been responsible for bringing another new profile to the world's oceans, that of the multi-decked super-structure, exaggeratedly flared, clipper-like stems and a plethora of funnel types, either disguised or having observation lounges or cocktail bars as an integral feature. The days of the trans-Atlantic liner were numbered with the advent of jet aircraft. Uneconomic and expensive to maintain they have no place in today's mercantile fleets. The *Norway/ex-France* is one of the few to have survived in service, though it is used primarily for cruising rather than Atlantic crossings. Some, like the record-breaking *United States*, are mothballed while others, including the *Queen Mary* have become static tourist attractions. They are all that remains of an era when ocean travel meant elegance, luxury, style and adventure.

Famous Clyde Built Liners

Abbreviations

PS   Paddle Steamer
SS   Single Screw
TSS   Twin Screw
TrSS Triple Screw
QSS   Quadruple Screw

Tonnages and Complements

Figures for tonnages and passenger complements are based on those issued at the commencement of service. Sometimes tonnage figures quoted in the text are at variance with those on the accompanying illustrations. Shipping lines often produced postcards of new vessels in advance of their entry into service so that details of size and tonnage given are approximations and therefore not particularly accurate. The figures quoted in the text are *gross tonnages*.

Company Liveries

	FUNNELS	HULLS
Allan Line	Red/Black top separated by white band	Black, red underbody and white waterline
Anchor Line	Black	Black, red waterline
Blue funnel Line	Light blue/black top	Black, red waterline
Canadian Pacific Line	Buff yellow, black top on earlier ships	Black, red underbody and white waterline
Cunard Line	Red with black top and stay rings	Black, red underbody and white waterline
Donaldson Line	Black with white band	Black, red waterline
Ellerman Line	Light brown/black top and white band	Bluish grey, red waterline
Orient Line	Buff yellow	Black, green waterline
P & O Line	Black	Black, red waterline
New Zealand Shipping Co	Yellow	Black, red underbody and white waterline

PS Britannia, 1840

Tonnage:	1,154 tons
Length:	207 feet
Beam:	34 feet
Speed:	8.5 knots
Machinery:	Two cylinder, side lever steam engine
Complement:	115

The first vessel ever commissioned for Cunard's trans-Atlantic service was this sturdy little wooden paddle steamer. She was one of four ships built to order by Robert Napier of Glasgow, although the construction of the hulls was sub-contracted out to other yards. These four, *Acadia*, *Britannia*, *Caledonia* and *Columbia*, were pioneers of the Royal Mail steam packet trade. *Britannia* resembled a sailing ship having three masts, a clipper bow and a guilded square stern, but there the similarity ended for she possessed two large and robust paddle wheels and a large non-raked smoke stack. On her maiden voyage from Liverpool to New York on 4th July 1840 she carried a mere 63 passengers and did the crossing in 12 days and 10 hours. *Britannia's* passenger accommodation was spartan to say the least and evidence of this survives in the diaries of her most illustrious passenger, Charles Dickens. He travelled to America in January 1842 and encountered en route one of the worst Atlantic storms which left him gravely sea-sick for much of the voyage. He described his cabin as 'an utterly impractical, thoroughly hopeless and profoundly preposterous box.' The dining salon was a 'hearse with windows', while the food was a 'smoking mess of hot collops' followed by a 'rather mouldy desert of apples, grapes and oranges.' Dickens, clearly not at his best, 'read in bed a good deal; and reeled on deck a little; drank cold water and brandy with unspeakable disgust and ate hard biscuits perseveringly: ill, but not going to be.'

The *Britannia* made 40 round trips to America under the Cunard houseflag before being sold to the Germans who renamed her *Barbarosa*. Her machinery was removed and she spent her last years as a sailing ship in the Prussian Navy before being sunk as a target ship in 1880.

PS Scotia, 1861

Tonnage:	3,871 tons
Length:	400 feet
Beam:	47.8 feet
Speed:	13.5 knots
Machinery:	Side lever steam engine
Complement:	300

During the 1850's and 1860's Robert Napier's yard produced some of the finest, fastest and most elegant vessels of the the time such as the *Arabia* (1853) and the *Persia* (1855). While these were successful vessels, none was more so than the iron-built *Scotia*, which was launched on 25th June 1861. She has been described as the 'last and finest paddle-driven vessel of the Cunard Steamship Company' and she was to serve her owners for some thirteen years. *Scotia* had a most pleasing silhouette. Her clipper bow was capped by a delicate bowsprit and figurehead while her masts, both fore and aft, carried two square yards. The design of her counter stern was to be copied by many shipbuilders well into the next century, while her widely spaced, pencil slim funnels gave her an aristocratic appearance. On her maiden voyage in 1862 she broke all records, completing the return trip to New York in 8 days and 3 hours and held the Blue Riband for the next five years. This much loved ship was finally laid up in 1875 and subsequently sold to the Telegraph Construction and Maintenance Company for use as a cable layer. The forty foot diameter paddles were removed and she was fitted with twin screws and a new set of engines. *Scotia* was still laying cables eighteen years later when a tremendous explosion blew her bows off, but she survived this and was extensively rebuilt. Her long career finally came to an end when she was wrecked in a storm off the island of Guam in 1904.

SS Umbria, 1884

Tonnage:	8,127 tons
Length:	519 feet
Beam:	57.3 feet
Speed:	19.5 knots
Machinery:	Three cylinder compound engine
Complement:	1,350

The *Umbria* and her sister *Etruria* were products of John Elder and Company and were the largest ships to be designed by the Managing Director Sir William Pearce. Both were built of steel and were among the last single screw vessels to ply the North Atlantic. Their place in the history of the ocean liner is assured inasmuch as they were the first ships to adopt a profile which would be copied by subsequent generations of liners. If either ship were to dock on the upper reaches of the Clyde today they would not appear altogether archaic. Yet, they still carried three masts and enough sail to ensure continued passage should engine failure occur. Cabins on both vessels were steam heated and lit by a combination of gas and electricity. In 1892 *Etruria* made the Atlantic crossing from Liverpool to New York in six days and twenty minutes. By the end of the nineteenth century both ships were regarded as out-of-date, largely due to the startling pace of liner development in the 1890's and were consigned to Cunard's secondary roster. They remained in service for a few more years before being sent to the breakers, *Etruria* in 1909 and *Umbria* in 1910.

TSS Ophir, 1891

The *Ophir*, named after a goldfield in New South Wales, was a truly beautiful ship of quite revolutionary design. She was built by Robert Napier and Sons and launched on 11th April 1891. *Ophir* entered service on 6th November of that year with a voyage from London to Sydney via the Suez Canal and Melbourne. She became instantly popular, partly because of her modern appearance. Gone were the older styles of four masts and yards and closely set funnels. Instead *Ophir* had two widely spaced funnels, heavily raked masts and an upright stem, though she retained that most attractive vestige of the days of sail-the elliptical or counter stern. A major drawback was that she was an uneconomical ship and a heavy consumer of coal throughout her career.

In 1901 *Ophir* enjoyed a brief moment of glory as the Royal Yacht which carried the future King George V and Queen Mary to Australia for the opening of the Commonwealth Parliament. The reason for her selection was that she was a twin-screw vessel, the first ever to operate on the Australia route, and she was thought to be extremely safe; her boiler rooms were over sixty feet apart and

ORIENT-ROYAL MAIL LINE S.S. OPHIR
AT CONSTANTINOPLE

Tonnage:	6,814 tons	Machinery:	Two triple expansion engines/twin screw
Length:	465 feet	Complement:	230 first class
Beam:	53.5 feet		142 second class
Speed:	18 Knots		520 steerage

a longitudinal watertight bulkhead divided the engine rooms. Painted white with a royal blue band around her hull and capped with buff coloured funnels, the ship looked magnificent. The royal cruise made *Ophir* a household name and certainly boosted the receipts on her return to commercial service. During the early years of the new century she was used mainly for cruising the Norwegian coastline, but she sailed to Australia in September 1907 before being laid up because of her high running costs. In January 1915 *Ophir* was requisitioned as an armed merchant cruiser and was attached to the 9th Cruiser Squadron intercepting suspicious merchantmen. She went to Gibraltar for an extensive refit in March 1916 and then returned to naval duties. In the final year of the war she was employed as a hospital ship and when the conflict ended the Admiralty chose to purchase her outright. *Ophir* left Devonport on her final voyage to Troon on the Clyde on 21st January 1919 where she was paid off three weeks later. The ship languished at Troon for a further three years before being sold for scrap and broken up on the spot.

TSS Campania, 1892

The *Campania*, which was launched on 8th September 1892, and her sister *Lucania* eclipsed every other liner on the North Atlantic when they entered into service in 1893. Both were products of Fairfield Shipbuiding and Engineering Company and were built at enormous expense. For a time the company was financially crippled as construction costs exceeded the tender price for both vessels by some £40,000. Owned by Cunard they were, when built, the largest and fastest ships in the world. Of the two, *Campania* had the edge with a maximum speed of 23.2 knots. She was an impressive looking vessel sporting two huge stacks, twenty feet in diameter, which towered 130 feet above the waterline. Her promenade deck featured two rows of massive ventilators, similar to the later Cunarder *Mauretania* and she offered passengers a degree of luxury never before enjoyed on the trans-Atlantic service. Both *Campania* and *Lucania* were fitted throughout with electric lighting, then something of a novelty, and boasted suites of cabins for the wealthier traveller; 75% of the passenger areas were devoted to first class passengers. As an added safety feature *Campania's* hull was subdivided into eighteen watertight compartments any two of which could be flooded without risk of sinking.

Tonnage:	12,950 tons	
Length:	620 feet	
Beam:	65 feet	
Speed:	23.2 knots	

Machinery:	Triple expansion engine/twin screw
Complement:	600 first class
	400 second class
	1000 steerage

The *Campania* took the Blue Riband in 1893 for the fastest crossing from Sandy Hook to Queenstown, averaging 21.9 knots. In 1897 she was one of the eleven liners in position at Queen Victoria's Diamond Jubilee when Charles Parsons' *Turbina* demonstrated the effectiveness of the steam turbine engine which was soon to replace the older triple expansion engine used on both Cunard sisters. Three years later *Campania* collided with the barque *Embleton* in the Irish Sea, slicing the boat in two and killing eleven of her crew. The *Lucania* fell victim to a disastrous fire while moored at Liverpool pier in 1909. *Campania* soldiered on but was finally sold for scrap in 1914. A reprieve came when the Admiralty decided to buy the ship and convert her into an aircraft carrier bearing the name *HMS Campania*. In November 1918 her anchor chain broke during a storm in the Firth of Forth causing her to drift on to the forefoot of *HMS Revenge*. She began to take in water by the stern and quickly sank.

TSS Tunisian, 1900

Tonnage:	10,576 tons
Length:	520 feet
Beam:	59.2 feet
Speed:	16.9 knots
Machinery:	Triple expansion engines (Stephen)/twin screw
Complement:	240 first class
	200 second class
	1000 steerage

The *Tunisian* was built by Alexander Stephen and Sons for the Allan Line. She was launched on 17th January, 1900 and set out on her maiden voyage from Liverpool to Halifax, Nova Scotia on 5th April that year. After an uneventful fourteen years of service she was conscripted as a troop transport and carried out this role for the next three years, during which time her owners were taken over by the Canadian Pacific Line (1st October, 1905). The ship was extensively reconstructed in 1920, being given new boilers and converted to oil-firing by D & W Henderson of Glasgow. Two years later her name was changed to *Marburn* and she continued to operate on the North Atlantic until 1927 when she was laid up off Southend. The *Marburn* returned to service briefly in 1928 when she was employed on the Antwerp-Canada service, but by May of that year she was once again idle. The next five months were spent on the maritime equivalent of death row at Southampton and on 17th September she proceeded to Genoa to be broken up by SA Co-op Demolitori Navi.

TSS Columbia, 1902

In 1901 the Anchor Line placed an order with the yard of D & W Henderson, with which it had strong links, for the construction of a new vessel for its North Atlantic Service. She was launched on 22nd February 1902 and given the name *Columbia*. The ship was to become one of the best known and loved liners of her day and from her maiden voyage in May 1902 until the outbreak of war she regularly plied the route from Glasgow to New York, replacing the older *City of Rome* which, from the outset of her career, had proved an uneconomic ship. *Columbia* berthed at Yorkhill Quay and was a familiar sight to all river traffic. She sailed from Glasgow on Saturday afternoons usually to the accompaniment of cheers and applause, for she was the flagship of what many regarded as Scotland and the Clyde's most illustrious shipping line. The only tense moment she experienced in those pre-war years came in 1911 when she collided with an iceberg and crushed her bow to a depth of some eighteen feet, flooding her number one hold in the process, but she reached New York safely.

Columbia served as an armed merchant cruiser for the duration of the war and was attached to the Atlantic Squadron of the US

Tonnage:	8,497 tons
Length:	485.5 feet
Beam:	56.3 feet
Speed:	16.5 knots

Machinery:	Triple Expansion engines/twin screw
Complement:	345 saloon
	218 second cabin
	740 steerage

Navy. To avoid confusion with their vessel USS *Columbia* the liner was temporarily renamed *Columbella*. In August 1919 she resumed her North Atlantic service and was the only Anchor liner on this route to have survived the war. After a period of some six years she was sold to the Byron Steam Ship Company, a subsidiary of the National Steam Navigation Company of Greece, and renamed *Moreas*. From September 1926 she operated on the Piraeus to New York run before being laid up the following year. Her career resumed albeit briefly in 1928 when the Greek company ran her once more on the New York service, but in July 1929 she was finally withdrawn and towed to Venice where she was broken up.

TrSS Virginian, 1904

The *Victorian* and her sister ship *Virginian* marked a turning point in the story of the modern ocean liner. It was a tribute to the Board of Directors of the Allan Line that they had sufficient confidence in the claims of Sir Charles Parsons, inventor of the steam turbine, to authorise the installation of this revolutionary means of propulsion in both vessels. The Workman, Clark Company of Belfast built the *Victorian* and it is this ship which is shown in the illustration; her identical sister was a product of Alexander Stephen and Sons. The *Virginian* was launched in December 1904 and completed her maiden voyage from Liverpool to St John, Canada in April of the following year. On the outbreak of war in August 1914 she was conscripted as a troop transport but three months later commenced work as an auxiliary cruiser with the 10th Cruiser Squadron. In October 1915 she was purchased, along with all other vessels of the Allan Line, by Canadian Pacific although she continued in naval service until 1920. In February of that year she was sold to the Swedish-American Line and renamed *Drottingholm*. During the Second World War she was in the service of the International Red Cross and upon cessation of hostilities was sold to the Home Line who renamed her *Brazil*. She undertook her first voyage for her new owners in 1948, from Genoa to South America and two years later was employed on the Naples to New York service. The vessel underwent a further change of name in 1951. As the *Homeland* she commenced service between Hamburg and New

ALLAN LINE

VICTORIAN

Tonnage:	10,754 tons	Machinery:	Parsons turbine engine/triple screw
Length:	538 feet	Complement:	426 first class
Beam:	60.3 feet		286 second class
Speed:	19.8 knots		1,000 third class
			250 crew

York under the management of HAPAG, the Hamburg-America Line. She was finally withdrawn from service in 1955 and on 29th March arrived at Trieste for breaking up.

TSS Carmania, 1905

The *Carmania* and *Caronia* were sister ships which provided their owners with an opportunity to measure the effectiveness of one power source against another. Cunard directors were deeply divided over the form of propulsion to be installed in their proposed superliner *Lusitania*. The engineering staff at John Brown and Company were known to favour the new turbines but a compromise was reached when it was agreed to fit alternative forms of machinery into the *Carmania* and *Caronia*, both then under construction at the yard. *Caronia* would have reciprocating engines while *Carmania* would be the experimental ship. The latter proved to be slightly faster, by 3/4 of a knot, and had a lower fuel consumption. Since her engines took up less space the *Carmania* was also the more economical cargo carrier. These factors aside, the two ships were among the most graceful of their day, earning for themselves the soubriquet 'The Pretty Sisters'.

Carmania was launched on 21st February 1905 and commenced her maiden voyage for Cunard on 2nd December when she left Liverpool for New York. Working in tandem with the *Caronia* she continued on this route until the outbreak of war in 1914. She then served as an auxiliary cruiser in the Royal Navy. It was in this guise that she was to achieve memorable status for she took part in the only gunnery exchange between two armed merchant cruisers. *Carmania*, armed with eight 4.7 inch guns and secondary armament, chanced on the *Cap Trafalgar*, in peacetime the flagship of the Hamburg-South America Line, armed with two 4.1 inch guns, six pom-poms and two machine guns. The liners met off Trinidad and in an action lasting for two hours *Carmania*, in spite of receiving seventy-nine hits, succeeded in sinking the German vessel. Badly damaged and on fire she turned away from the scene which had cost the lives of nine of her crew. German losses were sixteen. For the rest of the war *Carmania* served as a troop transport and then returned to civilian duties. The liner served on the Liverpool-Quebec route

Tonnage:	19,566 tons	Complement:	300 first class
Length:	675 feet		350 second class
Beam:	72.2 feet		900 third class
Speed:	22 knots		1,100 steerage
Machinery:	Parsons Turbines/ triple screw		700 crew

in the early twenties, the Liverpool-New York-Quebec route in the mid-twenties, the Liverpool-New York route in the late twenties and latterly cruised out of New York to the West Indies. She was finally broken up in 1932.

TSS Empress of Ireland, 1906

The *Empress of Ireland* was launched from Fairfield's yard in January 1906. Built for the Canadian Pacific Line, she was their largest vessel to date. She embarked on her maiden voyage from Liverpool to Quebec on 29th June 1906. The *Empress* continued to operate on that route until May 1914 when she fell victim to one of the worst maritime disasters in history. On the night of 29th May she was rammed by the Norwegian collier *Storstad*, while sailing down the St Lawrence river. The liner heeled over so rapidly that it was impossible to launch the lifeboats on her port side. Most of her passengers were preparing for bed at the time of the collision and so were below deck. Moreover, many of the portholes were open thus aiding the inrush of water as the ship listed. It took just over fourteen minutes for the *Empress* to sink, taking 1,024 passengers with her. At the subsequent Court of Enquiry the master of the *Storstad* was found guilty of negligent navigation while Captain Kendall of the *Empress* had no charge to answer. The tragedy never assumed the proportions of the *Titanic* two years earlier and today few people are even aware of it. Kendall's name appears elsewhere in the annals of maritime history for it was he who informed the authorities of the presence on board the *Montrose*, an earlier command, of the murderer H H Crippen and his accomplice Ethel Le Neve, both wanted for the murder of Crippen's wife. This made news headlines in 1910 as it was the first time that radio had been used to catch a criminal.

Tonnage:	14,191 tons	Machinery:	Quadruple expansion engines
Length:	570 feet	Complement:	310 first class
Beam:	65.7 feet		500 second class
Speed:	20 knot		270 steerage

QSS Lusitania, 1906

The *Lusitania* was the wonder ship of her day. She was much larger than any liner of the time when she was launched and provided greater luxury for all classes of passenger than any other ship afloat. Before her sister *Mauretania* arrived on the scene she could also claim to be the fastest. It is hard today to appreciate the excitement generated by her first appearance on the Atlantic but she was a very special ship. The sleek hull and four, tall well-raked stacks conveyed a feeling of speed and urgency. In an age where the horse was still supreme on land this technological masterpiece seemed to come from some future time. Her internal appointments were the subject of news reports, articles and gossip and there can be little doubt that in this respect she far outshone her rival. After much discussion Cunard, in consultation with the Admiralty, had offered the contract to build the *Lusitania* to John Brown and Company. Cunard wanted to revive Britain's merchant marine which during the previous decade had experienced strong competition from its German rivals and was in danger of losing the contest all together. The navy wanted a vessel which could, in the event of war, be converted into an auxiliary cruiser. Plans submitted by the Clydebank yard fulfilled both requirements. The ship was launched in June 1906 and in October of the following year took the Blue Riband for the fastest crossing between Queenstown and the Ambrose Light with an average speed of 23.99 knots. On the return voyage the 'Lucy' broke the east-west record with 23.61 knots; her top speed was reputed to be 26.35 knots.

The *Lusitania* was never taken up by the Admiralty for use as an auxiliary cruiser in World War One, possibly because of her size and fuel consumption. Instead she remained on the Liverpool-New York run with six of her boilers shut down, thereby reducing her speed to 21 knots. On 7th May 1915, while under the command of Captain William Turner, she was torpedoed off the Old Head of Kinsale (southern Ireland) by the U-20 commanded by Kapitan Leutnant Walther Schweiger. The great liner sank within eighteen minutes with the loss of 1,198 passengers and crew. Warnings had been issued in the American press that passengers travelling on British ships did so at their own risk but these went unheeded. The German Imperial Government always maintained that the ship had

CUNARD LINE.

Tonnage:	31,550 tons
Length:	787 feet
Beam:	87.8 feet
Speed:	26.35 knots
Machinery:	Steam Turbines/Quadruple screw

Complement:	563 first class
	464 second class
	1,138 third class
	802 crew

been carrying munitions for use on the western front, a claim the British authorities were quick to deny. Although the evidence suggests that the British Government may have contrived to create an incident which would ultimately bring America into the war, the fate of the *Lusitania* is still regarded as one of the first examples of 'total war'.

TSS Orsova, 1908

Tonnage:	12,036 tons
Length:	553 feet
Beam:	63.3 feet
Speed:	18 knots
Machinery:	2 sets of quadruple expansion engines/twin screw
Complement:	268 First Class
	120 Second Class
	660 Third Class

Orsova was the first of a class of six sturdy vessels built for the Orient Line in the years preceding World War One. Her sisters were *Otway*, *Osterley*, *Otranto*, *Orvieto* and *Orama*. They were indeed handsome ships having straight stems, twin buff-coloured funnels, black hulls with white upperworks and elegant counter sterns. Built at John Brown's yard, *Orsova* was launched on 7th November 1908 and undertook her maiden voyage from London to Brisbane,

Australia in June of the following year. During the war she acted as a troopship and it was on a homeward bound voyage from the Antipodes in March 1917 that she was torpedoed by a German U-boat, just off the Eddystone Light. The port side of her engine room was holed, killing six of the duty crew, but her master, Captain A J Coad, managed to beach her in Cawsand Bay inside Plymouth Sound. She was subsequently refloated and towed to Devonport for repairs. In January 1919 she resumed work ferrying Australian troops back home and in November undertook her first commercial post-war voyage to Brisbane. Her career lasted almost seventeen more years but by June 1936 she was old, outdated and exhausted. She was the last of the Orient Line's coal burners and the time had come for her disposal. *Orsova's* last voyage was to Bo'ness on the Firth of Forth where she was broken up by Douglas and Ramsey after twenty seven years of excellent service in which she had carried 14,000 tons of mail, 300,000 tons of cargo and, excluding war service, 70,000 passengers.

SS Rotorua/ex-Shropshire, 1911

Tonnage:	11,911 tons
Length:	526.4 feet
Beam:	61 feet
Speed:	14 knots
Machinery:	Quadruple expansion engines/twin screw
Complement:	120 first class

The *Shropshire* and her sister *Wiltshire* were built and engined by John Brown and Company for the Federal Steam Navigation Company in 1911 and a third sister, *Argyllshire*, was ordered by the Shire Line. There was nothing new or revolutionary about any of the three. All had quadruple engines which consumed about 100 tons of coal per day to propel the ships at their somewhat low maximum speed. Although rather lack-lustre ships they could be impressive when viewed from certain angles. The *Shropshire* had three continuous decks with six holds beneath these, four of them insulated. She was launched on the 27th April 1911 leaving on her maiden voyage on 28th October for Australia. Her life on the Liverpool-Australia route was short lived however, as she was requisitioned by the Admiralty in 1914. When peace returned the *Shropshire* was transferred to the New Zealand run under new owners, the New Zealand Shipping Company, who had gained control of the Federal Steam Navigation Company in 1912. In company with four other vessels she maintained a regular monthly service to New Zealand, but with a change of name. As the *Rotorua* she was extensively overhauled in 1922, converted to oil firing and given substantially improved passenger accommodation. She became a popular unit of the New Zealand Line's fleet until the arrival of the much larger *Rangitiki* and her sisters in 1929 whereupon she was converted to a one class ship. *Rotorua's* career ended on 11th December 1940 when she was torpedoed by the U-96, 110 miles west of St Kilda, sinking in twenty minutes. Nineteen of the crew were lost while the remaining 106 were picked up by naval rescue craft.

While hardly a beauty, the *Rotorua* did have a distinctive profile sporting no less than five topmasts. These gave her a rather dated appearance and were reduced in number as her career progressed.

QSS Aquitania, 1913

The *Aquitania* completed the trio of Cunard four stackers and was without doubt one of the finest ships ever to leave the ways at John Brown's. She was known as the 'ship beautiful' for she had a grace and elegance that few vessels could match. No expense had been spared on her internal fixtures and fittings. The impending

Tonnage: 45,647
Length: 901 feet
Beam: 97 feet
Speed: 24 knots

Machinery: Steam turbines/quadruple screw
Complement: 618 first class; 614 second class; 1,998 third class; 972 crew

launch of *Aquitania* was a source of consternation to the management of the Vulkan Yard at Hamburg who were then building the *Imperator*, a liner of some 52,000 tons designed to outstrip all other trans-Atlantic traffic. It was rumoured that the British leviathan would be twelve feet longer than the German ship, although 7,000 tons lighter. In an effort to ensure that the *Imperator* would be a winner on all accounts the Vulkan designers decided to incorporate into her bows an eighteen foot long, gilt-bronzed German eagle clutching a globe, on which the words 'Mein feld ist die Welt' were emblazoned. This ugly appendage, which adversely affected the stability of the ship, was short lived for on the *Imperator's* third Atlantic crossing a freak wave consigned most of the monstrosity to the deep. When the *Aquitania* was launched on 21st April 1913 German fears proved groundless as the British ship was a full eight feet shorter than the *Imperator*-sans eagle. With a maximum speed of 24 knots *Aquitania* was considerably slower than her two consorts *Lusitania* and *Mauretania*, but what she lacked in speed she made up for in luxury.

Her maiden voyage from Liverpool to New York began on 30th May 1914 but by August of that year she had been requsitioned by the navy as an auxiliary cruiser, in which role she lasted only a month. During 1915 she served as a troop transporter to the Dardanelles and then as a hospital ship. She returned to trooping duties the following year but was laid up for most of 1917. June 1919 saw her return to service as a member of the mercantile marine initiating the Southampton to New York route and in November she docked at the Armstrong Whitworth yards in Newcastle for conversion to oil firing. On the first voyage after this work there was an explosion in her engine room which killed a crew member. Thereafter she settled down to uniterrupted service and to become one of the most popular liners of the next two decades. Royalty, Hollywood stars, politicians and sports personalities all travelled on her. In the mid-twenties she offered a weekly service in tandem with Cunard's flagship *Berengaria* and the *Mauretania* to the States. The *Berengaria* was in fact her former rival *Imperator* which had been handed over to Britain as part of the war reparation in 1921. Cruising figured in the schedule occasionally, particularly to the Mediterranean.

The *Aquitania* was paired with the *Queen Mary* in 1934, although it was Cunard's intention to scrap the ship after the *Queen Elizabeth* had been completed and put into service. Her life was extended when she was used again as a troop transport in the Second World War and she continued in government service until 1948. In her last years she provided cheap economy fares for British GI brides but was a mere shadow of the ship that was. As one crewman remarked "It's only the rust that's holding her together". Her final voyage from Halifax to Southampton was completed on 1st December 1948. The *Aquitania* had steamed over 3 million miles and crossed the Atlantic 475 times in a long career which ended in the breakers at Faslane on 21st February, 1950.

Cunard R. M. S. "Aquitania". 46,647 Tons.

TSS Ormonde, 1917

Tonnage:	14,853 tons
Length:	600 feet
Beam:	66.6 feet
Speed:	18 knots
Machinery:	Geared turbines/twin screws
Complement:	278 first class
	195 second class
	1000 third class

The *Ormonde* was laid down at John Brown's yard in May 1913 but, because of the outbreak of war the following year, was not completed until 1918. For that period she had only the basic accommodation required for the role of troop transport. In November 1919 she finally sailed on her maiden voyage with the mails and a full complement of passengers on the route she was to become closely identified with-London to Brisbane. Over the next three years she was to make a further nine round trips together with a short season of cruises to the Norwegian fjords in the summer of 1922. In April 1923 she returned to her builders for conversion to oil firing and then resumed her programme of cruising. For the next ten years she continued to operate on the Tilbury to Sydney/Brisbane run before being converted to a one class ship in 1933. On September 23rd, while off Gabo Island near Cape Howe, New South Wales, a fire which proved difficult to extinguish broke out in her number four hold. The Commonwealth liner *Murada* stood by in case it was necessary to evacuate passengers and crew but the fire was eventually brought under control enabling the *Ormonde* to continue her voyage to Sydney.

An immensely popular ship, *Ormonde* served with distinction throughout the inter-war period before being called upon once more for war service in 1939. She was no longer a young ship and the punishing schedules forced on her by the Admiralty took their toll. After a refit in 1947 it was obvious that her future was limited. The Australian Government required ships for immigration purposes, due to the enormous demand for assisted passages, and had requested permission to charter *Aquitania*. This request was refused by the British Government who offered instead three vessels: *Ranchi*, *Chitral* and *Ormonde*. In October 1947 *Ormonde* left Tilbury with over 1000 emigrants on board. Fares for the passage ranged from £59 to £95. By August 1952 the emigrant boom was over and after 35 years of sterling service so too was *Ormonde's* career. Her last voyage took her to Dalmuir where she was broken up in December 1952.

TSS Tyrrhenia/Lancastria, 1920

To most people *Tyrrhenia* will be an unfamiliar name for the ship, whose sinking remains one of the worst ever sea tragedies, was far better known as the *Lancastria*. Built by William Beardmore and Company and launched on 31st May 1920, she was an unexceptional vessel which had originally been intended for the Anchor Line as a sister to their *Cameronia*, but was purchased by Cunard before completion for their Canadian service. *Tyrrhenia* was therefore, the first Cunarder to have a cruiser stern. Her first voyage for that company was from Hamburg to New York in 1923, but the following year she was renamed *Lancastria* and began a weekly service from London to New York with the *Carmania*, *Caronia* and the Anchor Line's *Tuscania* as running mates. From 1932 until 1939 she was used almost exclusively for cruising, often sporting a white hull.

Tonnage: 16,243 tons
Length: 578 feet
Beam: 70.2 feet
Speed: 17 knots
Machinery: Geared turbines/twin screw

Complement: 265 first class
370 second class
1,150 third class
320 crew

73

Lancastria was requisitioned when war broke out and entered service as a troop transport in May 1940. On 17th June she was attacked by German bombers off St Nazaire and after suffering four direct hits sank in twenty minutes. The liner *Oronsay* and the cargo ship *John Holt* were able to rescue 2,477 survivors including the *Lancastria's* master, Captain Randolph Sharp. However, to this day no one knows how many died in the attack or even how many were aboard at the time. Official figures put the death toll at around 2,500 but the Association of Lancastria Survivors believes that the true figure is nearer 5,000 out of a total complement of approximately 9,000. It is thought that most of those who died were burned alive in a sea heavily polluted with fuel oil. The British people only learned of the disaster one month later and even then only veiled accounts were released for fear of damaging public morale. Winston Churchill described the sinking as 'the most terrible disaster in our naval history'.

TSS Tuscania, 1921

Tonnage:	16,991 tons
Length:	580 feet
Beam:	70.2 feet
Speed:	17 knots
Machinery:	Geared turbines/twin screws
Complement:	240 first class
	377 second class
	1,818 third class
	346 crew

Tuscania was launched from the Fairfield yard on 4th October 1921. Both she and her sister *California* were the first of projected new tonnage for the Anchor Line at the beginning of the decade. Her maiden voyage took place in September 1922 on the Glasgow to New York route and during the peak seasons she continued to operate on the North Atlantic, although the occasional trip from Liverpool to Bombay was also included. Unfortunately the Anchor Line management were never quite sure what role the vessel should play in their fleet, as she was somewhat superfluous to their needs, so she tended to be used only as a relief ship. From 1926 to 1930 she was placed under an extended charter to Cunard for their London-New York trade before being laid up for almost a year until August 1931. From this time she was used mainly for cruising although she did undertake several more voyages from Liverpool to India.

She was sold in April 1939 to the Greek Line who renamed her *Nea Hellas* and operated her out of Piraeus, but in 1941 the British Ministry of Transport requisitioned her for war work and she was only returned to the Greek owners in August 1947. During the war years she carried thousands of troops to whom she was affectionately known as the 'Nellie Wallace'. As the *Nea Hellas* she plied the Mediterranean route to New York until 1955 when she was replaced by the Greek Line's new flagship *Olympia*, a product of Alexander Stephen and Sons. In her final years she served on the Bremerhaven-New York run and was renamed again in 1955, this time adopting the name *New York*. The ship was finally laid up in the autumn of 1959 and a career which spanned nearly forty years ended when she was sent to the breakers at Onomichi, Japan in October 1961.

TSS Athenia, 1922

Athenia was a product of the Fairfield yard and was launched on 28th January 1922. She was one of a pair of vessels built for the Glasgow-based Donaldson Line for service on the Glasgow to Montreal route, the other being the *Letitia*. Both were fine looking ships having straight stems, centrally placed superstructures, funnel and no forecastles. Internal fittings were economic but both were excellent sea boats. *Athenia's* maiden voyage, from Glasgow to the St Lawrence, took place in April 1923 and she continued to operate

Tonnage:	13,465 tons
Length:	538 feet
Beam:	66.3 feet
Speed:	16 knots
Machinery:	Geared turbines/twin screws
Complement:	516 cabin class
	1000 third class
	300 crew

on this route until 1939 when war broke out. While outward bound for Canada on 3rd September 1939, the day war was declared, she was torpedoed by the U-30, 200 miles west of the Hebrides. 112 lives were lost and survivors were landed at Halifax in Canada on 14th September, having been picked up by the freighter *City of Flint*. The sinking outraged many on both sides of the Atlantic as most of her passengers were child evacuees being conducted to the safety of the New World. Further, it was widely known that Berlin had given strict orders that no action be taken against unarmed passenger ships for the time being. At the time the German High Command denied responsibility for the attack; only after the war did the German Government admit that they were responsible for the loss of the *Athenia*.

TSS Patroclus, 1923

Tonnage:	11,314 tons
Length:	530 feet
Beam:	62.3 feet
Speed:	15.5 knots
Machinery:	Geared turbines/twin screw
Complement:	140 first class
	80 crew

There are few more instantly recognisable ships than those of the Blue Funnel Line with their characteristic tall, non-raked stacks, clean hull forms and Greek mythological names. The *Patroclus*, built by Scott's of Greenock and launched on 17th March 1923, was a typically fine example of marine design in the *Blue Funnel* tradition. Her half-sisters were the *Sarpedon* (Cammel Laird), *Hector* (Scott's) and *Antenor* (Palmer of Newcastle); all were of the passenger-cargo type and operated out of their home port of Liverpool on routes to the Far East. The *Patroclus* entered service on this route in June 1923 and gave sixteen years of unstinting service until being called up as an armed merchant cruiser on the outbreak of war. Her naval career was short lived however, for she was torpedoed by the German submarine U-99, 150 nautical miles west of Ireland on November 4th 1940. She was hit while rescuing survivors from the armed merchant cruiser *Laurentic* which had been torpedoed a few hours earlier by the same U-boat. It took a further five torpedoes and five hours before the *Patroclus* finally sank, her hold being filled with empty barrels which maintained her buoyancy.

TSS Chitral, 1925

Tonnage:	15,248 tons
Length:	548 feet
Beam:	70.2 feet
Speed:	16 knots
Machinery:	Quadruple expansion engines/twin screws
Complement:	199 first class
	135 second class

The *Chitral* was built for the P & O Line by Alexander Stephen and Sons of Linthouse and was launched on 28th January 1925. Intended for the London to Sydney route, she spent almost her entire life on this run. In 1930 she was fitted with additional low pressure turbines which added another knot to her speed. On the outbreak of war she served as an armed merchant cruiser on the northern patrol and in an early encounter on 20th November 1939 she intercepted the German ship *Bertha Fisser*, which was disguised as a Norwegian freighter. After the crew abandoned ship *Chitral* sunk her with gunfire. Four days later she picked up eleven survivors from the *Rawalpindi* after that ship's classic engagement with the German pocket battlecruisers *Scharnhorst* and *Gneisenau*. In March 1940 she assisted with 'Operation Rivet', transporting troops to Iceland, and in November was called upon to search for survivors of Convoy HX 84 which had been attacked by the *Admiral Scheer* (among the vessels in this convoy was the famous *Jervis Bay*). Refitted in California in October 1941 she returned to the Clyde and then spent what was left of her naval career east of Suez. During the early post-war years she was de-commissioned and refitted again as a one-class emigrant ship. She inaugurated this service in December 1948 with a voyage from London to Sydney. By the early 1950's *Chitral* was mechanically exhausted and had outlived her usefulness. She was sold to be broken up at Dalmuir in April 1953.

TSS Transylvania, 1925

Tonnage:	16,923 tons
Length:	552 feet
Beam:	70.2 feet
Speed:	17 knots
Machinery:	Geared turbines/twin screw
Complement:	279 first class
	344 second class
	800 third class

During the early twenties the Anchor Line commissioned the building of the *Tuscania*, from Fairfield, and the *California*, from Stephen's, for their Glasgow to New York service. Both were rather severe looking vessels built as workhorses of the Atlantic rather than ocean greyhounds and in consequence passenger receipts for the pair were lower than expected. The North Atlantic was always the most glamorous of shipping routes and required that ships reflect this image. The Anchor Line board, determined not to make the same mistake twice, ordered two further steamships from the two yards. The *Transylvania* was launched from Fairfield's in March and the *Caledonia* from Stephen's in April 1925. Their interior accommodation was typical of the Anchor Line style, with extensive wood panelling and veneering but provided for the passengers slightly more plush surroundings than they had come to expect from the company's earlier liners. Surprisingly, the only noticeable deviation from the profiles of their predecessors was the presence of three funnels rather than one.

Transylvania undertook her maiden voyage from Glasgow to New York on 12th September 1925. Her career was uneventful until the outbreak of war when she was requisitioned as an armed merchant cruiser. She first saw action on 15th October 1939 when she sunk the German ship *Poseidon* after an ill-fated attempt to take her in tow. On her second outing she stopped the German *SS Teneriffe* which was posing as the Swedish ship *Gunor*, but before a prize crew could be put on board the Germans scuttled her. The following year she rescued forty-one members of the German ship *Mimi Horn* which was so fiercely ablaze that no boarding party could be put aboard. During the early months of 1940 *HMS Transylvania* underwent a major refit in Belfast followed by engine repairs on the Clyde. On 9th August she set sail for the northern patrol grounds and had just passed Ailsa Craig running at 16.5 knots. Steering a course of 262 degrees she altered course around midnight during which a double explosion occurred somewhere along her port side. Although crippled the ship was taken in tow in an attempt to beach her but she eventually sank, somewhere between Malin Head and Islay. It is believed that forty eight of the crew went down with the ship. The assumption was that *Transylvania* had been the victim of a U-boat attack but none was seen at the time. Only after the war was it confirmed that the U-56 had inflicted mortal damage on this fine ship.

TSS Duchess of York, 1928

Tonnage:	20,021 tons
Length:	601 feet
Beam:	75.1 feet
Speed:	19 knots
Machinery:	Geared turbines/twin screws
Complement:	580 cabin class
	480 tourist class
	510 third class
	510 crew

The *Duchess of York* was built by John Brown and Company for the Canadian Pacific Line in 1928. She was one of a class of four, the others being the *Duchesses of Atholl, Bedford* and *Richmond*, all of which were Clyde built. The *Duchess* was launched on 28th September 1928 and in March 1929 she sailed on her maiden voyage from Liverpool to St John. Originally it had been the intention to name her *Duchess of Cornwall* but the name had been dropped only days before she was launched. She gave twelve years of unstinting service on the North Atlantic before being requisitioned as a troop transport. It was during this period, on a voyage from Glasgow to Freetown, that the *Duchess of York* was attacked by German long range bombers some miles west of Oporto and set on fire. All but eleven of the crew were saved thanks to the quick intervention of the destroyers *Douglas* and *Iroquois* and the frigate *Moyola*. The ship continued to burn and was abandoned the following day, 12th July 1943. It remained only for a convoy escort to torpedo and sink the smouldering hulk of this stately vessel. Of her class only two ships survived, the *Bedford* and the *Richmond*. The former saw further service as the *Empress of India* and subsequently the *Empress of France*, while the latter achieved post-war fame as the *Empress of Canada*.

QSS Empress of Britain, 1930

Tonnage:	42,348 tons	Machinery:	Geared turbines/quadruple screws
Length:	760 feet	Complement:	465 first class
Beam:	97.4 feet		260 tourist class
Speed:	25.5 knots		470 third class
			740 crew

The *Empress of Britain* was the largest ship ever to operate on the Canadian sea route. She was launched by the Prince of Wales on 11th June 1930 in a ceremony which was broadcast throughout the British Empire. The *Empress* was the pride of the CPR fleet and it was hoped that her sumptuous accommodation and size would lure American and Canadian passengers away from the more popular New York routes to Europe by persuading them to travel east from Quebec. Sadly the plan failed to work and the liner proved to be an albatross around the company's neck for she was an expensive ship to run and rarely sailed with anything like her full complement of passengers. She was a particularly unattractive vessel having three huge stacks which were surely too big for her hull and superstructure, and an ugly cruiser stern. The ship looked best at night when floodlit but the cold light of day highlighted only too clearly her aesthetic shortcomings.

A product of John Brown's yard the *Empress* set off on her maiden voyage in May 1931 from Southampton to Qubec. During the winter months she undertook cruising duties. These usually took the form of a four month world cruise at a cost of $2,000 per passenger and to reduce fuel costs her outer propellers were removed. Leaving New York the *Empress* would sail for the Mediterranean, pass through the Suez Canal then on to India and Hong Kong, China and Japan, Hawaii and California, pass through the Panama Canal and then home once more. Inevitably on the outbreak of war she was called up for troopship duties and met her unfortunate end on 28th October 1940. When returning from Canada to Britain she was attacked by a German long range bomber seventy nautical miles north-west of Ireland and set on fire. Her passengers and crew were forced to take to the lifeboats and were picked up by rescue ships. The Polish destroyer *Burza* took the burning liner in tow but this rescue bid was thwarted by the U-32 which torpedoed and sank the *Empress* with the loss of forty nine crewmen.

QSS Queen Mary, 1934

Tonnage:	80,744 tons
Length:	1,019 feet
Beam:	118.1 feet
Speed:	32 knots
Machinery:	Parsons geared turbines/quadruple screws
Complement:	776 cabin class; 784 tourist class; 579 third class; 1,101 crew

She wasn't the biggest of the pre-war liners-that title fell to her near sister *Queen Elizabeth*-and for sheer elegance and style she was some way removed form her French rival *Normandie*, the most glamorous ship of the decade. However, the *Queen Mary* had a personality and an appeal which brought her a sizeable loyal following and gained for her an almost reverential position in the roster of great liners. Laid down at John Brown's yard in December 1930, but not launched until 26th September 1934, she was regarded with pride and affection by the British public, her very existence being taken as a symbol of triumph in the face of adversity. In appearance the *Mary* differed little from what had gone before and to some she was merely an enlarged version of Cunard's older flagship *Berengaria*. Nevertheless she was an imposing sight and emerged the only superliner of the period to show a profit for her owners. The maiden voyage from Southampton to New York at the end of May 1936 was a glorious affair culminating in a near hysterical reception in the American city. In August of the same year a record west-east crossing averaging 31.69 knots won her the Blue Riband from the *Normandie*, although the French ship regained it in March and July 1937 for the eastern and western crossings respectively. Not to be outdone the *Queen Mary* covered the west-east trip at 30.99 knots in August 1938 and did the return journey at a remarkable 31.69 knots, a record which stood until July 1952.

In September 1939 the liner was laid up in New York because of the war, but secretly sailed to Sydney for fitting out as a troop transport. She and her sister, the only ships capable of carrying an entire division of 15,000 troops, performed magnificently in this capacity. Their importance in this role was such that Hitler offered the Iron Cross, First Class and a reward of $250,000 to any U-Boat captain who could sink either vessel. The *Normandie* never performed a similar role. While being converted for war work by the US Navy she was accidentally set on fire and capsized at her New York berth on 10th February 1942. Eight days before this tragedy a disaster of greater human proportions befell the *Queen Mary*. While sailing twenty miles north-west of Bloody Foreland (Northern Ireland), on a voyage from the USA to the Clyde, the ship's alarm was sounded to give warning of enemy submarines in the vicinity. As an avoidance action the *Mary* adopted a zig-zag course which caused her to bear down on her anti-aircraft escort, the old cruiser *Curacoa*. The escort was cut in two and sank within minutes; 364 of the crew died out of a full complement of 390. The submarine warning proved to be a false alarm.

Queen Mary was released for commercial service in September 1946 and returned to her builders for an overhaul and a refit. Ten months later she embarked on her first post-war voyage from Southampton to New York, a service she continued until 1967. By this time rising costs and poor passenger receipts were contributing to losses in the region of $2 million per annum. Consequently Cunard decided to sell the liner to the City of Long Beach, California for the sum of $3.5 million. She arrived there early in November 1967 and work commenced to convert her into a shipping museum, hotel and convention centre. This venture survives at the time of writing.

SS City of Benares, 1936

Tonnage:	11,081 tons
Length:	509 feet
Beam:	62.7 feet
Speed:	17.25 knots
Machinery:	Geared turbines/single screw
Complement:	219 one class
	180 crew

The *City of Benares*, launched from the yard of Barclay, Curle and Company on 5th August 1936, was to become the flagship of the Ellerman Line. She was one of the company's most popular passenger-cargo liners, operating on the Liverpool to Bombay route without incident until the outbreak of war. On 17th September 1940 she was sailing in convoy to Canada with hundreds of children aboard. They were being evacuated, under the auspices of the Children's Overseas Reception Board, to the safety of North America. Some 600 miles out in the Atlantic the *City of Benares*, the leader of the convoy carrying its Commodore and his staff, was torpedoed by the U-48. The torpedo struck No 5 hold on the ship's port side at approximately ten o'clock at night when most of the children were asleep. Alarm gongs sounded and passengers and crew took to the lifeboats; an hour later the ship sank leaving the survivors to cope in appalling weather conditions. There had been 406 passengers on board of whom 248 died in this tragedy. 77 children were among the dead. Some boats drifted for days before being picked up. The experience of one of these bears repeating.

Fourth Officer Cooper took command of one of the lifeboats in which there were six children, a passenger, a cadet, a sea-man gunner, the assistant steward, a navy signalman and thirty-two of the *Benares* Lascar crew. Food and water had to be strictly rationed and although the children were in high spirits the situation looked serious. While the foul weather continued unabated, Cooper sailed the lifeboat on an easterly course in the hope of reaching land. Eventually after a week and with emergency rations running low the boat was sighted, still 400 miles from land, by a Coastal Command Sunderland which sent a destroyer to rescue them.

TSS Circassia, 1937

Tonnage:	11,137 tons
Length:	506 feet
Beam:	65.9 feet
Speed:	18 knots
Machinery:	Doxford diesels/twin screws
Complement:	321 first class
	80 steerage

This vessel, launched on 8th June 1937, was produced by Fairfield's for the Anchor Line. She was Anchor's first motorship and was built as a passenger-cargo liner. *Circassia* and her two sisters, *Cilicia* and *Caledonia*, were immediately successful giving excellent service until disposed of in the mid-1960's. Her maiden voyage from Liverpool to Bombay began on 23rd October 1937 and she remained in service on this route until January 1940 when she was commissioned as an armed merchant cruiser, a role she was to play for the next two years. Then she served as a troop transport until 1943 when she was modified as a large Infantry Landing Ship. In 1948 *Circassia* resumed the Liverpool-Bombay run and on Jan 13 1966 made the Anchor Line's last passenger sailing on this route, thus ending a 110 year old service. This also marked the end of the ship's career as she was then sold for £140,000 and broken up at Alicante in April of that year.

QSS Queen Elizabeth, 1938

Although for many years the world's biggest passenger ship, the *Queen Elizabeth* never quite garnered the praise heaped on her half-sister *Queen Mary*. Launched from John Brown's yard on 27th September 1938, she was part of Cunard's scheme to have a two ship trans-Atlantic service. Whereas the *Mary's* maiden voyage took place amidst a blaze of publicity, the *Elizabeth* was dispatched secretly to the United States without having undergone her trials. She was in the final stages of fitting out in late February 1940, six months after war had been declared against Germany, when she made this famous dash to safety. It is said that while en route to the States she met the battleship *HMS Queen Elizabeth*. As both had orders to maintain radio silence the warship passed a one-word message by signal lamp-'Snap'! To confuse the enemy the story was put about that the *Elizabeth* was undertaking a positioning voyage to Southampton and on the day that she should have arrived there Luftwaffe bombers were circling overhead in readiness for an attack. Once in New York she was prepared for a trip which would take her to Sydney via Singapore, there to be fitted out as a troop transport. The *Mary* and the *Elizabeth* then embarked on a gruelling schedule of trans-Atlantic crossings ferrying US troops to British shores while returning sometimes with German or Italian prisoners

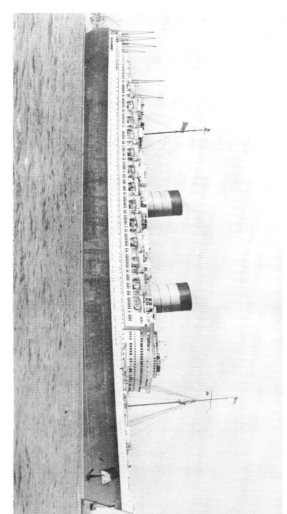

Tonnage:	83,763 tons
Length:	1,029 feet
Beam:	118.4 feet
Speed:	32 knots

Machinery:	Parsons geared turbines/quadruple screw
Complement:	823 first class
	662 second class
	798 tourist class
	1,296 crew

89

of war. At one point it was proposed to convert her into an aircraft carrier but this, thankfully, came to nothing. The war years also saw her assigned to the Indian Ocean troop service operating between Sydney and Suez, Freemantle and Tricomalee. Both the Queens were targets for sabotage. Two bombs were found under a pile of blankets aboard the *Elizabeth* in April 1943, holes were discovered in the lifeboats and fire extinguishers vandalised; this despite an armed guard of 250 servicemen when the liner was berthed in New York.

After the war *Elizabeth* was the first Cunarder to be released from service and after re-fitting at Southampton and Gourock sailed on her post-war maiden voyage to New York in October 1946. Her final voyage for Cunard was in December 1968 after twenty years of impeccable service. The following July she was sold to Queen Limited, Port Everglades for use as a conference centre but by August the firm was bankrupt. The *Elizabeth* was then sold off at auction, for £1.3 million, to the Chinese shipowner C Y Tung who intended to use her as a floating university based in Hong Kong. Upon arrival there work started on her conversion, but on the 9th January 1971 fire broke out which soon spread throughout the entire ship. The next day she heeled over, flames still spouting from her hull she continued to burn for the next three days thus ending her chances of salvage.

TSS Caronia, 1947

Caronia was Cunard's first purpose-built cruise ship and a product of John Brown and Company. She was launched by Princess Elizabeth on 30th October 1947, undertook her trials a year later and left Southampton for New York on her maiden voyage on 4th January 1949. Right from the start her livery was four shades of green which earned her the nickname 'Green Goddess' and she boasted the tallest mast and the largest funnel of any ship afloat. The *Caronia* quickly became very popular with the wealthy set. She cruised for the first three months of each year either to the Pacific, Africa or around the world. In May followed a six-week stint on the Mediterranean and Black Sea cruise schedule, while June was time for her six week Scandinavian cruises up the Norwegian fjords and

Tonnage:	34,183 tons
Length:	715 feet
Beam:	91.5 feet
Speed:	22 knots

Machinery:	Geared turbines/twin screw
Complement:	581 first class
	351 second class
	600 crew

to the Baltic ports. In September she was back in New York preparing for further cruises in the Mediterranean and when these were completed she returned to Southampton for an annual refit before starting the cycle all over again. Her rich clientelle brought her the further nickname 'The Millionaires Yacht'.

Despite her popularity she was an uneconomic ship to run having fuel bills and an average of only 400 passengers per cruise. *Caronia* was the first Cunarder to slip into the red in the late 1950's but because of her obvious prestige the company was prepared to bear her losses. However, by the mid-sixties the punishing schedule was beginning to take its toll and she was sent to Harland and Wolff's Belfast yard for an extensive refit which included the modernisation of her passenger facilities. She re-appeared in December 1965 ready to return to duty but the cruising market was changing with newer, even more luxurious vessels arriving on the scene. Two years later Cunard had had enough and took the decision to withdraw the ship from service and put her up for sale. The Yugoslavian company Domus-Turist showed some interest and had plans to use her as a floating hotel at Dubrovnik but the project collapsed. *Caronia* was finally purchased in May 1968 by the Universal Line, a Greek company, who first of all renamed her *Columbia* and shortly afterwards *Caribia*. She was refitted at Piraeus before embarking on a cruising schedule in the Caribbean. On the second such trip there was an explosion in her engine room which killed a member of the crew and disabled the ship. She was towed back to New York and laid up in March 1969. There she remained until January 1974 when she was sold to breakers in Taiwan. Before leaving New York for Kaohsiung her interiors were stripped bare and her fittings auctioned off. On 12th August, while in tow, the ship encountered heavy weather causing her to leak badly. In an effort to escape the worst of the storms the master of the towing vessel *Hamburg* took the decision to make for Guam in the Pacific. As both tug and liner approached the entrance to Apra harbour the larger vessel struck the breakwater, heeled over and sometime later broke in three, thus bringing to an inglorious end the career of one of the truly great ships.

TSS Saxonia, 1954

Tonnage:	21,637 tons
Length:	497 feet
Beam:	80.4 feet
Speed:	22 knots
Machinery:	Geared turbines/twin screw
Complement:	110 first class
	819 tourist class
	461 crew

17th February 1954 saw the launching of the first of a new Cunard quartet from John Brown's. Her name was *Saxonia*, the fifth vessel to bear that name, and Lady Churchill performed the ceremony. Later members of the group, *Ivernia*, *Carinthia* and *Sylvania* were also built at the same yard. Each had a domed funnel, high superstructure compared to earlier Cunarders, a short, rather stubby mast and nicely raked stem. *Saxonia's* maiden voyage was in September 1954 on the Liverpool to Montreal route but from 1957 Southampton became her British terminal. She embarked on her first crossing from Liverpool to New York in 1961 and the following year returned to her builder for a refit, emerging with a bright green hull and a new name, *Carmania*. Her first voyage in this new colour scheme was from Rotterdam to Montreal and later in the year she undertook cruises from US ports. On 14th January 1967 the ship ran aground off San Salvador with 471 passengers aboard and stuck there for four days before being refloated. She proceeded to New-port News, Virginia for repair though the damage was superficial. Subsequently she sported an all white-hull and was used for cruising only but four years later was laid up and offered for sale.

The four sisters could never be regarded as successful and this was mainly due to the advent of jet aircraft, which reduced Atlantic travel to hours rather than days, in the late fifties. *Saxonia/Carmania* was eventually purchased by a Panamanian Company which had acquired the ship for the Soviet State Shipping Company. She was renamed the *Leonid Sobinov* and after her first voyage from Southampton to Sydney for her new owners undertook extensive cruising in the Pacific and Far Eastern waters.

TSS Queen Elizabeth 2, 1967

<table>
<tr>
<td rowspan="2">SOUTH EAST ENCLOSURE</td>
<td>* Gates open from 1 p.m. to 1.50 p.m.
Admission by ticket only.
Children under 7 years not admitted.</td>
<td>(ENTER BY CART STREET)</td>
<td>THE CUNARD STEAM-SHIP COMPANY LIMITED
JOHN BROWN & CO. (CLYDEBANK) LIMITED

Launch of

Cunard Liner No. 736

from Clydebank Shipyard
on Wednesday, 20th September, 1967
at 2.30 p.m. *

This card admits **one person**
It is to be shown at Entrance Gate (Cart Street)
and given up on entering South East Enclosure.
See back for directions</td>
</tr>
</table>

A tinge of sadness surrounded the launch of the *QE2* for she was the last of the truly great Clyde-built ships; within a short time even the name of her builder, John Brown and Company, would be consigned to the history books. She was launched on 20th September 1967, undertook her trials between November and December 1968 and despite some teething troubles with her turbines, entered service on 23rd December with a cruise from Greenock to the Canary Islands. Her glory was short-lived however, as she suffered further turbine failures which forced a return to her builders.

Tonnage:	65,863 tons
Length:	963 feet
Beam:	105 feet
Speed:	32.4 knots

Machinery:	As built-geared turbines/twin screw; from 1986-diesels
Complement:	564 first class
	1,441 tourist class
	906 crew

95

Cunard then refused to accept the ship but after renewed trials in early April 1969 delivery of the vessel was made and a much publicised second 'maiden' voyage from Southampton to New York took place in May. Unlike the two previous Queens the *QE2* is used mainly for cruising. On 9th January 1971 she helped to rescue passengers and crew from the burning French liner *Antilles* in the Caribbean but was herself in need of assistance in April 1974 when her boilers were put out of action 270 miles south west of the Bermudas. Temporary repairs failed to hold and 1,654 passengers had to be transferred at sea to the Norwegian liner *Sea Venture*. The *QE2* was then towed to Hamilton for repairs. January 1975 saw the ship undertake her first world cruise, now an annual event.

After her first visit to Philadelphia in April 1982 she returned to the UK and was requisitioned by the British Government for service in the Falklands. Within eight days she was given two helicopter platforms, military satellite receivers and equipment to refuel at sea. She set sail on 12th May with over 3,000 troops on board. On her return voyage home the *QE2* carried 640 survivors of the sunken warships *HMS Coventry, Antelope* and *Ardent* and after an emotional welcome at Southampton she went for an eight week refit. When the ship re-appeared it was in a new livery of light grey hull, white superstructure and funnel painted for the first time in traditional Cunard colours, though the hull colours did not last long as it was difficult to maintain on the North Atlantic. In 1986 the great ship sailed for Germany to undergo major engineering alterations. Her steam turbines were costly to operate and Cunard felt that, if the ship were to continue in service, she would need to be converted to diesel power. After long months of work the *QE2* emerged as a motor vessel sporting a white funnel of chunkier girth than the original. To this date she continues to sail primarily as a cruise ship.

POSTSCRIPT

The Years of Decline

The First World War increased the capacity of the Clyde yards by a third but it was not possible to exploit this in the years of recession which followed. Between 1920 and 1933 output slumped from 680,466 tons per annum to 48,770 tons. Yard closures and amalgamations, which meant unemployment for thousands of shipyard workers, were an inevitable response to the crisis.

Shipyard Workforce (Glasgow)

1919	43,000
1930	29,000
1936	16,000
1939	24,000

Demand for both naval and merchant shipping was stimulated by the Government in the years leading up to the Second World War, though it can be seen from the above figures that this did not bring a return to full production. However, all the Clydeside yards, including those previously closed, were pressed into service during the war and they made an outstanding and immeasurable contribution to the war effort.

The demand for replacement vessels ensured that the shipbuilding boom continued after 1945 but the Clyde yards failed to cash in on it. There was a marked reluctance to invest in new plant and equipment after the experience of the early twenties. Competitors such as Japan, West Germany and Scandinavia, with the benefit of heavy subsidies, adopted new mass production techniques and exploited their advantage to secure a share of what had hitherto been a British dominated market. When the Clyde yards did realise that the boom was to be a sustained one they misjudged market needs. They built liners when it was becoming apparent that the future of long-distance passenger travel lay with air transport; dredgers when up-river terminals were closing in favour of deep water ports; ferries when roads, bridges and tunnels were reducing dependence on these. By the 1960's the yards were making huge losses as a result of fixed priced contracts, poor labour relations, rising material costs and, in some cases, a reluctance to accept new technology.

In 1967 the Geddes Committee, set up by Harold Wilson's Labour Government, recommended that the yards of John Brown, Yarrow, Charles Connell, Alexander Stephen and Fairfield be amalgamated to form Upper Clyde Shipbuilders Ltd. The committee was highly critical of each firm's performance in the post-war period, accusing them of short-sightedness and poor market forecasting. UCS came into being in 1968 but the consortium proved disastrous for all. Each yard had little in common with its fellow members; Yarrow was a naval yard, Brown's and Fairfield were both in the passenger liner market while Stephen's and Connell's built mostly cargo vessels. Yarrow withdrew from UCS in 1971 and the consortium collapsed the following year. In an attempt to salvage something from the wreckage Fairfield and Connell merged to form Govan Shipbuilders while John Brown was taken over by Marathon (UK) Ltd (and later by UIE (France)). Lithgow's and Scott's on the lower Clyde remained independent as did Yarrow but the first two subsequently amalgamated on the advice of the Geddes Committee.

World markets for ships declined in the 1970's with even the powerful Japanese feeling the effects. The once profitable tanker market slumped after oil prices rocketed in 1974, while the oil and gas rig boom proved to be short lived. In 1977 Callaghan's Labour Government took the decision to nationalise British Shipbuilding. Since 1979 the privatisation policy of Mrs Thatcher's Conservative Government has led to Scott-Lithgow being sold off to the Trafalgar House Group (also owners of the Cunard Line) and Yarrow Shipbuilders Ltd being acquired by GEC. At the present time Clyde shipbuilding is operating at a fraction of its post-war capacity; one writer has forecast, 'it is likely that by the 1990's there will be no merchant ship yards left on the Clyde, and perhaps no yards at all'. It can only be hoped that this gloomy prediction is not fulfilled.

APPENDIX ONE

Principal Clyde Shipbuiders since 1900

Ailsa Shipbuilding Co Ltd	Ayr	1902-1929
Alley and Maclellan Ltd	Polmadie, Glasgow	1890-1960
American Marine and Machinery Co	Paisley	1964-1969
Anglo-Dutch Offshore Concrete Construction	Hunterston	1975-1978
Appledore-Ferguson	Port Glasgow	1986-
Ardrossan Dockyard Ltd	Ardrossan	1925-1964
Ardrossan Drydock and Shipbuilding Co Ltd	Ardrossan	1899-1925
Sir William Arroll and Co Ltd	Meadowside, Glasgow	1941-1945
Ayrshire Dockyard Co Ltd	Irvine	1928-1934
Barclay, Curle and Co Ltd	Whiteinch, Glasgow	1855-1967
William Beardmore and Co Ltd	Govan/Dalmuir,Glasgow	1900-1930
Bergius Launch and Engine Co	Glasgow	1908-1939
Blythswood Shipbuilding Co Ltd	Scotstoun, Glasgow	1919-1964
George Brown and Co (Marine) Ltd	Greenock	1900-1983
John Brown and Co Ltd	Clydebank	1899-1968
Caird and Co Ltd	Greenock	1888-1922
Campbeltown Shipbuilding Co Ltd	Campbeltown	1877-1922
Campbeltown Shipyard Ltd	Campbeltown	1968-1967
William Chalmers and Co Ltd	Rutherglen	1903-1920
Clyde Shipbuilding and Engineering Co	Port Glasgow	1900-1929
Charles Connel and Co Ltd	Scotstoun, Glasgow	1861-1968
William Denny and Brothers	Dumbarton	1865-1963
Dunlop, Bremner and Co Ltd	Port Glasgow	1911-1926
Fairfield Shipbuilding and Engineering Co Ltd	Govan, Glasgow	1886-1965
Fairfield (Glasgow) Ltd	Govan, Glasgow	1966-1968
Ferguson Brothers (Port Glasgow) Ltd	Port Glasgow	1903-
Ferguson-Ailsa Ltd	Troon and Port Glasgow	1981-
Fleming and Ferguson Ltd	Paisley	1885-1969
John Fullarton and Co	Paisley	1866-1929
Govan Shipbuilders Ltd	Govan, Glasgow	1972-
Greenock Dockyard Co Ltd	Greenock	1920-1966
William Hamilton and Co Ltd	Port Glasgow	1871-1963
Harland and Wolff Ltd	Govan, Glasgow	1912-1962
Harland and Wolff Ltd	Greenock	1922-1936
J & J Hay	Kirkintilloch	1868-1958
D & W Henderson and Co Ltd	Meadowside, Glasgow	1873-1962
A & J Inglis Ltd	Pointhouse, Glasgow	1862-1962
James Lamont and Co Ltd	Port Glasgow	1929-1979
Lithgows Ltd	Port Glasgow	1915-1972
Lobnitz and Co Ltd	Renfrew	1895-1957
London and Glasgow Engineering and Iron Shipbuilding Co Ltd	Govan, Glasgow	1864-1912

Hugh Maclean and Sons Ltd	Govan, Glasgow	1880-1943
Archibald McMillan and Son Ltd	Dumbarton	1834-1930
Marathon Shipbuilding Co (UK) Ltd	Clydebank	1972-1980
Napier and Miller Ltd	Yoker/Old Kilpatrick	1898-1930
Alex Noble & Sons ltd	Girvan	1946-
Port Glasgow Shipbuilding Co	Port Glasgow	1912-1927
Ross and Marshall Ltd	Greenock	1899-1925
Russell and Co	Greenock/Port Glasgow	1874-1918
Scotstoun Marine Ltd	Scotstoun, Glasgow	1973-1980
Scott Lithgow Ltd	Greenock/Port Glasgow	1969-
Scott's Shipbuilding and Engineering Co Ltd	Greenock	1711-1967
T B Seath and Co	Rutherglen	1856-1902
John Shearer and Son	Glasgow	1890-1907
William Simons and Co	Renfrew	1860-1957
Simons Lobnitz Ltd	Renfrew	1957-1963
Alexander Stephen and Sons Ltd	Linthouse, Glasgow	1851-1968
UIE Shipbuilding (Scotland) Ltd	Clydebank	1980-
Upper Clyde Shipbuilders Ltd	Clydebank, Govan, Linthouse, Scotstoun	1968-1971
Yarrow and Co Ltd	Scotstoun, Glasgow	1906-1979
Yarrow Shipbuilders Ltd	Scotstoun, Glasgow	1977-

APPENDIX TWO

Notable Vessels launched from Clyde Shipyards, 1812-1987

NAME	TYPE	BUILDER	LAUNCH	OWNER
Comet	coastal/pass	J Wood	1812	H Bell
-Wrecked off Craignish Point 1820.				
Industry	baggage boat	W Fife	1814	J Cochrane
Margery	channel steamer	W Denny	1814	_____
Vulcan	iron passage b't	T Wilson	1819	_____
-A replica of this vessel will be on view at the Glasgow Garden Festival and thereafter at Coatbridge where the original was built.				
HMS Greenock	iron warship	Scott & Sons	1849	Admiralty
City of Glasgow	pass steamship	Tod & McGregor	1850	Inman Line
-Disappeared with all hands, 1854.				
Arabia	pass steamship	R Steele & Co	1852	Cunard Line
-Last wooden hulled Cunarder.				
Brandon	pass/cargo st'mer	Randolph-Elder	1854	London-Limerick
-First steamer with compound engine.				
Persia	pass steamship	R Napier	1855	Cunard
-First iron hulled Cunarder.				
HMS Black Prince	armour-plated warship	R Napier	1861	Admiralty
Washington	pass steamship	Scott & Sons	1863	Cie Generale Transatlant.
-First twin-screw Atlantic liner.				
Ariel	tea clipper	R Steele & Co	1865	_____
-Disappeared in the Indian Ocean, 1872.				
Agamemnon	pass/cargo	Scott & Sons	1866	Blue Funnel
-Vertical tandem compound steam engine.				
Cutty Sark	tea clipper	Scott & Linton	1869	J Willis
Columba	coastal pass	J & G Thomson	1878	D. MacBrayne Ltd
Livadia	royal yacht	J Elder & Co	1880	Russian Imperial Royal Family
-A turbot-shaped vessel.				
Ravenna	pass/cargo	W Denny	1880	P & O Line
-P & O's first steel hulled ship.				
Aberdeen	pass/cargo	R Napier	1881	Aberdeen Line
-Early steam triple expansion engine.				
City of Paris	pass steamship	J & G Thomson	1889	Inman Line
Glen Sannox	coastal pass	J & G Thomson	1889	Glasgow & South Western Railway
-Fastest Clyde paddle steamer, 20 knots.				
HMS Cressy	armoured cruiser	Fairfield	1899	Admiralty
-Sunk by U-9, Sept 1914.				
King Edward	coastal pass	W Denny	1901	Turbine Steamers
-First passenger turbine steamer.				
HMS Arab	destroyer	J & G Thomson	1901	Admiralty
-Capable of 30 knots.				
HMS Good Hope	cruiser	Fairfield	1901	Admiralty

-Sunk at Coronel, Nov 1914.

Armadale Castle pass steamship	Fairfield	1903	Union-Castle

-The company's first liner.

HMS Indomitable battle-cruiser	Fairfield	1908	Admiralty

-Saw action at Jutland, May 1916.

HMS Colossus battleship	Scott & Sons	1912	Admiralty

-Also in action at Jutland.

HMS Tiger cruiser	John Brown	1914	Admiralty
HMS Swordfish submarine	Scott & Sons	1916	Admiralty

-First British steam submarine.

HMS Repulse battle-cruiser	John Brown	1916	Admiralty

-Sunk with Prince of Wales off Malaya, Dec 1941.

HMS Hood battle-cruiser	John Brown	1920	Admiralty

-Sunk during an engagement with Bismark and Prinz Eugen, May 1941.

Windsor Castle pass steamship	John Brown	1921	Union-Castle

-Last four funnelled British liner.

King George V coastal pass	W Denny	1926	Williamson Buchanan

-Later owned by David MacBrayne.

Empress of Japan pass steamship	Fairfield	1930	CPR
Lochfyne coastal pass	W Denny	1931	D. MacBrayne

-Turbo electric motor vessel.

Talisman coastal pass	A & J Inglis	1935	LNER then CSPC

-Diesel electric paddle vessel.

HMS Maidstone depot ship	John Brown	1938	Admiralty
HMS Implacable aircraft-carrier	Fairfield	1944	Admiralty
HMS Vanguard battleship	John Brown	1946	Admiralty
Waverley coastal pass	A & J Inglis	1947	LNER then CSPC

-Last ocean-going paddle steamer.

Uganda pass steamship	Barclay Curle	1952	British India

-Extensively used for student cruising.

Olympia pass steamship	A Stephen & Sons	1953	Greek Line
HMS Diana destroyer	Yarrow & Co	1954	Admiralty

Last of the 'Daring' class.

Pibroch puffer	Scott's of Bowling	1957	Scottish Malt Distillers
Bardic Ferry pass/car ferry	W Denny		1957 ASNC

-First British ro-ro ferry.

Glenfalloch cargo vessel	Fairfield	1962	Glen Line
HMS Ardent frigate	Yarrow & Co	1977	Admiralty

-Lost during the Falklands campaign.

HMS Broadsword frigate	Yarrow & Co	1979	Admiralty
Traquair liquid gas carrier	Ailsa and Ferguson Bros		1981 Anchor

-Ship built by both yards in two parts and then joined together at Inchgreen.

HMS Boxer 'stretched' Type-22 destroyer	Yarrow & Co	1982	Admiralty

-Improved design following the Falklands conflict.

Selkirk Settler bulk carrier	Govan shipbuilders	1983	Northern Great Lakes
Norsea pass/car ferry	Govan shipbuilders	1987	North Sea Ferries/P & O

-World's largest passenger ferry at the time of launching.

BIBLIOGRAPHY

The Face of Glasgow	Power and Eadie	Smith & Son (Glasgow), 1938
The Second City	Oakley	Blackie, 1976
Clyde Shipbuilding from Old Photographs	Hume and Moss	Batsford, 1975
Victorian and Edwardian Steamships from Old Photographs	Greenhill and Gifford	Batsford, 1979
Ocean Liners	Wall	Collins, 1977
Trans-Atlantic Paddle Steamers	Spratt	Brown, Son and Ferguson, 1980
The Liners	Coleman	Penguin, 1977
The British Seafarer	Mason, Greenhill and Craig	Hutchinson/BBC, 1980
Fifty Famous Liners (3 volumes)	Braynard and Miller	PSL, 1982/85/87
North Atlantic Run	J Maxtone Graham	Cassel, 1972
Queen Mary, Her early years recalled	Winter	PSL, 1986
RMS Queen Mary, Fifty Years of Splendour	Hutchings	Kingfisher Railway, 1986
The Great Luxury Liners 1927-1954	Miller	Dover, 1981
The First Great Ocean Liners in Photographs 1897-1927	Miller	Dover, 1984
Majesty at Sea (The Four Stackers)	Shaum and Flayhart	PSL, 1981
The Great Liners	Maddocks	Time-Life, 1978
Song of the Clyde	Walker	PSL, 1984
Passenger Ships of the Orient Line	McCart	PSL, 1987
20th Century Passenger Ships of the P & O	McCart	PSL, 1985
The Guiness Book of Ships and Shipping	Hartman(ed.)	Guiness, 1983
Historic Cunard Liners	Rentell	Atlantic Transport, 1986
Growth and Decline of Clyde Shipbuilding	Moss	SEB/Education for Industrial Society, 1986
Merchant Fleets (in Profile) especially:- No 1: P & O, Orient and Blue Funnel No 9: Anchor No 13: Donaldson	D Haws	TCL
Merchant Ships in Colour 1910-1929	Dunn	Blandford, 1973
North Atlantic Seaway (5 vols)	Bonsor	Brookside, 1976